STO ✓

FRIENDS
OF ACPL

D1539988

CARL LINNAEUS

Pioneer of Modern Botany

Carl Linnaeus in his later years. He is wearing his decoration as Knight of the Polar Star, and in his left hand holds his favorite flower, the twinflower, named for him, *Linnaea borealis*. An engraving from a copy of the original portrait at the Royal Academy of Sciences in Stockholm, Sweden.

CARL LINNAEUS
Pioneer of Modern Botany

by Alice Dickinson
Illustrated with photographs and drawings

Franklin Watts, Inc.
575 Lexington Avenue, New York, N. Y. 10022

PICTURE CREDITS

Frontispiece, The American Museum of Natural History; opp. page 1, and pages 43,
131, 168, 176, 184, and 188, The Bettman
Archive. The cover engraving is from The
Bettman Archive.

The drawings in Chapter 5 and the quotations on pages 159, 160, 171, 172, 192, and
193 are reproduced with permission from
the manuscripts in the Linnean Society of
London.

☐Designed by Joel Levy

Library of Congress Catalog Card Number: 67-18897
ⓒ Copyright 1967 by Franklin Watts, Inc.
Printed in the United States of America
1   2   3   4   5

CONTENTS

U. S. 1416968

FOREWORD

IN WRITING THIS BOOK I HAVE FOUND HELP
in many places. I am indebted to Mr. Theodore
O'Grady, Librarian of the Linnean Society of
London, England, for his hospitality and kind-
ness in making available to me the wealth of material in the Society's collection: Linnaeus' herbarium, his library, his annotated copies of his
own books, his handwritten, hand-illustrated
journal of his Lapland travels, and the hand-

written English translation of his autobiography — all invaluable.

Many of Linnaeus' own works have also been helpful. They are:

Linnaeus, Carl. *Bibliotheca Botanica*. Amsterdam: Salomon Schouten, 1736.

Linnaeus, Carl. *The "Critica Botanica" of Linnaeus.* Translated by Sir Arthur Hort; revised by M. L. Green. With an Introduction by Sir Arthur W. Hill. London: The Ray Society, 1938.

Linnaeus, Carl. *Fundamenta Botanica.* Amsterdam: Salomon Schouten, 1736.

Linnaeus, Carl. *A General System of Nature, through the Three Grand Kingdoms of Animals, Vegetables and Minerals, Systematically Divided into Their Several Classes, Orders, Genera, Species and Varieties with Their Habitations, Manners, Economy, Structure and Peculiarities.* Translated from Gmelin, Fabricius, Wildenow, together with Various Modern Arrangements and Corrections derived from the Linnean and Other Societies. 7 vols. London: Lashington, Allen, and Co., 1806.

Linnaeus, Carl. *Lachesis Lapponica, or A Tour of Lapland.* Translated by James Edward Smith. 2 vols. London: White and Cochrane, 1811.

Linnaeus, Carl. *Species Plantarum: A Facsimile of the First Edition, 1753.* With an Introduction by W. T. Stearn. 2 vols. London: The Ray Society, 1957.

Linnaeus, Carl. *Systema Naturae sive Regna Tria Naturae Systemice Proposita per Classes, Ordines, Genera & Species.* Leyden, 1735.

Pulteney, Richard. *A General View of the Writings of Linnaeus.* London: Printed for J. Mawman by R. Taylor and Co., 1805.

I have quoted from some of these works in this book. Other works that have been consulted are:

Caddy, Florence. *Through the Fields With Linnaeus.* 2 vols. London: Longmans, Green & Co., Ltd., 1887.

Gourlie, Norah. *The Prince of Botanists, Carl Linnaeus.* London: H. F. & G. Witherby Limited, 1953.

Gray, Asa. *Manual of Botany.* New York: American Book Company.

Hagberg, Knut. *Linnaeus.* Translated from the Swedish by Alan Blair. New York: E. P. Dutton & Company, Inc.

Jackson, Benjamin Daydon. *Linnaeus.* Adapted from the Swedish of Theodor Magnus Fries. London: H. F. & G. Witherby Limited, 1923.

Smith, James Edward. *A Selection of Correspondence of Linnaeus and Other Naturalists from the Original Manuscripts in the Linnean Society.* 2 vols. London, 1821.

Stoever, D. H. *The Life of Sir Charles Linnaeus.* Translated from the original German by Joseph Trapp. London, 1794.

A.D.

CARL LINNAEUS
Pioneer of Modern Botany

Linnaeus in his Lapland costume, with his so-called magic drum, probably used by him for carrying botanical specimens. Portrait painted by M. Hoffman in 1737.

WHAT IS ITS NAME?

IN NEW ENGLAND, JUST WHEN THE WINTER woods are misting green in spring, a cup-shaped, glossy-yellow flower appears in clusters to brighten the edges of marshes and brooks. New Englanders call the plant a cowslip, but the flower manuals say it is more generally known as a marsh marigold. Some manuals add, "Incorrectly called cowslip." Folk names die hard, though, and to many New Englanders the plant remains a cowslip.

The flower manuals do list a Virginia cowslip, but that is something else again. It has trumpet-shaped blue flowers.

The Virginia cowslip is also known as the Virginia bluebell, although one flower manual remarks that it is related neither to the English cowslip, which belongs to the primrose family, nor to the English bluebell, which belongs to the lily family, nor to the Scotch bluebell, which really is what it seems to be — a member of the bluebell family.

Confusing? Yes.

Again, in New England's August pastures there is a plant topped by a spire-shaped cluster of small rosy blossoms. Some people speak of it as hardhack, but others, mindful of those rosy spires of bloom reaching upward, call it steeplebush. When the two factions talk to each other about the plant, a little misunderstanding sometimes arises, and explanations and descriptions are necessary.

All over the world, people have their favorite names for plants, and often they have the same names for entirely different plants. It is no wonder that misunderstandings sometimes develop about which one is meant.

Plant scientists have a way out of this difficulty. They identify plants in Latin, the common language of botanists everywhere. Each plant has been given a definite botanical name made up of two parts. (Often the name is not classical Latin, but a Latinized form of some other words.) The name has been agreed to and is recognized by all plant scientists everywhere. So, when the cowslip-marsh marigold comes up for discussion, it is always known as *Caltha palustris,* which means "marsh cup," a wonderfully descriptive name. The Virginia cowslip-bluebell and the hardhack-steeplebush also have permanent scientific names known to all botanists.

When the botanical names are used, every plant scientist can quickly and easily understand exactly what plant is meant. No lengthy descriptions are necessary and no misunderstandings arise. These names are botany's code and shorthand, just as easy to learn and understand as any other name, if a person makes a slight effort in the beginning.

Botanists also find it helpful to think of individual kinds of plants in groups, the members of each group having important characteristics in common. There are yellow roses and yellow dandelions, for instance. But a yellow rose is more like a red rose than it is like a yellow dandelion. The two roses are similar in many ways more telling than their color. Botanists use a scientific method of describing and classifying that will take into account the basic likenesses between all the roses — such as their leaf and flower forms, and their way of growing — and will put them together in one group, clearly separate from the dandelions. And so it is with all other plants. Each has its place in a group among related plants. The botanical name of the plant indicates the place it occupies. Plants whose names begin with the same botanical word belong most closely together.

An orderly classification system of this kind makes it easier for botanists to work with their plant materials. It helps them reach an understanding of the many, many thousands of kinds of plants and the relationships among them. And too, when botanists discover a plant unknown to them, they can decide what it may be by finding the group whose description sounds most like it and by comparing it with the members already classified. In this way, a botanist may be able to find the exact scientific name of the plant. Or if the unknown plant proves to be one that has many characteristics in common with the others of the group, yet differs from them in some important way, it may possibly be a new member, and may be given a Latin name of its own, within that group.

The man who first successfully grouped plants in a simple and understandable order and consistently used the system of giving each plant a binomial — a name made up of two Latinized words that would remain fixed — was Carl Linnaeus, a Swedish botanist of the eighteenth century.

When he began his work, the classifying and naming of plants was in complete confusion. True, attempts had been made at arranging like plants into groups, and the plants often had Greek or Latin names in addition to the ones that ordinary people knew. There was no uniform

4

system of naming or arrangement, however. More often than not, each botanist went his own peculiar way. And sometimes the botanical names were impossibly long. In order to speak of a certain kind of plant, it was often necessary to give its description. For instance, one botanist called a certain weed, the plantain, *Plantago media incana virginiana, ferrata foliis, annua.*

Scores of other plants were known by descriptive terms just as awkward as the long name of that kind of plantain was, and botanical names threatened to become even more difficult to learn and remember as time went on. In Linnaeus' day, the windows on the world were opening. Starting in the fifteenth century, European explorers had gone out over the seas and had come back with wonder tales of new lands full of strange plants and animals. Now, in the 1700's, the botanists were following the explorers, or were going with them. From the four corners of the world, hitherto unknown plants were beginning to pour back to the Old World scholars. What should these plants be called? With so much that was new, the long Latin names would soon become impossible to use.

No one realized this more clearly than Carl Linnaeus. If ever a man appeared at the right time, it was he. Linnaeus had sharp, observant eyes; a passionate love for all green growing things; an eager, impulsive, up-and-doing nature; a deeply inborn sense of order; and a feeling for names.

"If you know not the names, the knowledge of things too is wasted," he said, and proceeded to stage a revolution in the botanical naming of plants. Out of the welter of possible terms that might have been chosen, he tried to pick the one that seemed best to point to an outstanding characteristic of a plant. To him, plants were personalities, each with its own odd foibles. He gave the seven-worded *Plantago* mentioned on page 5 the binomial *Plantago virginica*, because it was native to Virginia. (*Plantago* means "footprint," or "sole of the foot," in Latin; the plant probably was given the name because of its flat leaves.)

Linnaeus called the tobacco plant *Nicotiana tabacum*. It had been named *Nicotiana major latifolia* by an earlier French botanist. *Latifolia* means "broad-leaved." The name *Nicotiana* was given in honor of the French scholar and diplomat Jean Nicot, who had obtained seeds of the plant from a sailor in Lisbon, Portugal, in 1561, and had introduced tobacco culture into France. Linnaeus' name *"tabacum"* makes the point that this plant is tobacco. (*Nicotiana tabacum* is an example of a Latinized name. Neither part was originally Latin. *Tabacum* comes from the American Indian word for the plant.)

Out of the unwieldy Latin language, Linnaeus created a new botanical tongue, vivid, and responsive to the needs of that science. Through his system of naming, plants took on new meaning, not only because his names were descriptive and easy to learn and remember, but also because they showed something of a plant's relationship to certain other plants.

Into the botanic chaos of his day Linnaeus brought simplicity and order. He created a foundation on which later botanists could build. During his lifetime his system of classification and naming swept Europe. Not only scientists, but ordinary plant-lovers as well, could think of no higher honor than to send an unknown plant to be classified and named by Linnaeus, the famed teacher and botanist of the university at Uppsala, in Sweden. Because of his work, people all over England and the Continent, and in North America too, found a new fascination in knowing and growing plants. Because of him, botany took on new life and made giant strides toward becoming a modern science. It is small wonder that in his day Carl Linnaeus was known as "the Prince of Botanists."

Map of Sweden, about 1740.

"THE LITTLE BOTANIST"

FROM THE VERY BEGINNING OF HIS LIFE, CARL
Linnaeus seemed destined to be a botanist. Even
his family name could be traced back to a plant.

His father, Nils Ingemarsson, came from a
farming family — one who loved the soil but
had great respect for learning, too. In Ingemarsson's youth, in the late 1600's, surnames were
not common in Sweden except among scholars
and the aristocracy. The farmers usually added

only "son" to their fathers' names, or were called by the names of the farms where they lived. So, when Nils Ingemarsson decided to enter a university and become a Lutheran clergyman, the question of a proper surname for him arose. In those days it was customary for Swedish students to take Latinized names upon going into a church career.

On the land owned for many years by Nils's ancestors was an enormous and very ancient linden tree, famous for miles around. It was regarded with overwhelming awe and superstition by the farm people of the vicinity. They believed that great grief would come to anyone who harmed the tree in any way or took as much as a leaf from it. Even the tiniest twig that fell from its huge branches was returned reverently to the base of the tree by some passerby.

Paying recognition to this tree, some of Nils's relatives, who also had been bound for the university, had taken the name Tiliander, from the Latin word for "linden" — *tilia.* Another branch of the family had adopted the Latinized name Lindelius from the Swedish word *lind,* meaning "linden." So, when it was Nils Ingemarsson's turn to choose a name for the university register, he too paid reverence to the impressive old tree. He chose Linnaeus as his Latinized surname, from the Swedish word *lind.*

Nils Linnaeus was ordained a priest of the Lutheran church in 1704. A few months later he became the curate to the parish of Stenbrohult in the province of Småland, in southern Sweden. Less than a year after that he married seventeen-year-old Christina Brodersonia, the daughter of his superior, Stenbrohult's parish priest. She was a hardworking, orderly, highly intelligent girl, while Nils seems to have had something of the poet in his nature. He was gentle and quiet and loved gardens and the out-of-doors.

At first the young curate and his wife lived in a small cottage at Rashult, near the parish church at Stenbrohult. Around their dwelling, Nils laid out a garden. His delight was to find rare specimens to add to his growing plant collection. His wife too took great pleasure in their garden.

Here at Rashult, on May 23, 1707, the young couple's first child was born, "in a delightful season of the year," as he later wrote, "between the bursting forth of the leaves and the blossoming of the flowers." His parents named him Carl.

Soon afterward the child's grandfather, Pastor Brodersonius, died, and before long, Nils Linnaeus was appointed as his successor. Now the family moved to the rectory at Stenbrohult, a truly beautiful spot. The house and church stood by the side of a long inlet of Lake Möklen, which stretched away to the west. To the south, in this country of hill and dale, were beech woods with their smooth, soft-gray trunks; to the north rose a mountain ridge; to the east spread rich meadows; and beyond the meadows were dark pine forests and oak groves.

Carl Linnaeus never forgot the spreading lake and the summer meadows, bright with hundreds of flowers, and alive with the humming of insects and the winging and singing of birds. This scene remained vivid to him all his days — a kaleidoscope of color and motion. Nowhere could a child have had a better introduction to nature.

His father had early called the boy's attention to the world of growing things. Nils's greatest enjoyment was to work among the trees and flowers of his garden, and he shared his pleasure with his family. As he passed through the house he sometimes placed a fragrant blossom on the cradle of his infant son. When the boy was about a year old, his father often took him into the garden or the meadows. Nils Linnaeus loved his little son's companionship. Carl lay in the grass as his father worked, and to amuse him, Nils often handed him a flower to play with.

After the move to the Stenbrohult rectory, Nils laid out a much larger and more elaborate garden than the one at nearby Rashult. In this new garden there were fruits of many kinds, a thriving kitchen garden, ornamental trees, and flowers in great variety. As Carl grew a little older he wandered in the garden, watching his father work among the plants. At last he demanded a garden of his own, and Nils gave him a small flower bed to care for. The little boy watched his father carefully,

imitating his actions. He became such a good gardener
that later a section of land was set aside as "Carl's garden." Here he planted what he wished, and cared for it
in his own way. His garden became an absorbing part of
his life.

When Carl was old enough to walk through the fields
with his father he loved to hear Nils talk about the wild
flowers that the two of them found. The names had a
fascination for the child and he eagerly asked to know
what each newly found plant was called. At first, Nils
took pains to answer the boy carefully, but then he
realized that his little son forgot his replies almost as
soon as they were given. Nils spoke severely to the boy,
saying that he would no longer tell him the plant names
if Carl did not intend to remember them. Carl took the
scolding much to heart. From then on, he made an effort
to learn thoroughly the names of the plants he saw.

But the long days of freedom in the garden and
meadows were cut off all too soon. In 1714, when Carl
was seven, Pastor Linnaeus decided that his son's formal
education should begin. Both Nils and his wife had
agreed that the boy must be a clergyman, and this required solid learning. Johan Telander, a man of the
parish, was hired as a tutor. Years later, Carl Linnaeus
described Telander as "a morose and passionate man,
who was better calculated for extinguishing a youth's
talents than for improving them."

However that may be, the teaching did go badly. On

every possible occasion, Carl left his books and slipped out to the garden. His mother was greatly vexed with him, but his father felt a sympathy for the boy. At last, however, even Nils came to understand that Carl would never study as long as he remained at home, in the lovely Stenbrohult countryside that was proving so distracting. Accordingly, in 1716, Pastor Linnaeus sent his nine-year-old son with the tutor to the nearby town of Växjö. The arrangement was not a happy one. Johan Telander had little sympathy for small boys, and little patience with them.

Two years later, Telander had departed. Carl had been enrolled in the lower grammar school at Växjö. The boy still did not care for studying and whenever he could he escaped classes, to roam the fields. Among his schoolmates he became known as "the little botanist." At the end of five years he succeeded in passing to the middle school, however — graded eleventh in a class of fifteen.

In the higher school, Carl found much greater liberty to ignore classes. To him they seemed a waste of time when instead he might be outdoors, looking for plants that were new to him. As often as possible he left the town behind him and wandered in the fields and woods beyond it. But this was no idle wandering. Carl Linnaeus had uncommonly keen eyes and a quick brain. Already, too, he had at least the beginnings of an idea of what he wanted from life. He was training himself to notice even the tiniest plants. During his school days at Växjö he made himself intimately acquainted with the plant life growing for miles around, and knew where each kind of native plant might be found.

Soon after Carl entered the grammar school, Daniel Lannerus, a friend of his father's, had been appointed Rector of the Lower School. He took pity on the unhappy little boy and did what he could to help him. The Rector was an amateur botanist himself. He noticed Carl's great interest in all growing things, and often invited the boy into his garden. There the two talked about plants. At last, impressed by Carl's knowledge of botany, Lannerus spoke of him to Johan Rothman, the state doctor of Småland, and a lecturer and senior master at the Växjö High School.

All during his youth, Carl Linnaeus seems to have possessed an almost magical quality. His magic was entirely unconscious, to be sure. It was probably a blend of bubbling enthusiasm, extraordinary intelligence, high spirits, and a lively responsiveness to the world and people around him. Whatever it was, at various crucial moments in his life young Carl Linnaeus appears unfailingly to have attracted to himself some older person who was well equipped to help him at that time. Dr. Rothman was just such a person. He met Carl and was strongly drawn to him.

Rothman, too, had a garden, and he too was impressed by Carl's knowledge of botany. Through the years, Carl had managed to buy a few botanical books, which he had studied carefully. His schoolwork still failed to interest him, however. By the time he reached high school the studies were mostly such as would prepare a boy to be a clergyman. Rhetoric, logic, Hebrew, and theology — these were not subjects in which Carl Linnaeus excelled. He did well in what mathematics and physics were taught, and he received good training in Latin. Later the Latin he learned proved useful to him in his botanical work; like all the scholars of his time he wrote and spoke the language fluently, though, in his case, not always accurately. Many of the books he eventually published were written in Latin.

Dr. Rothman realized that young Carl lacked the interest to be anything but a mediocre clergyman. As a physician himself, however, the schoolmaster recognized the boy's aptitudes. Carl had a leaning toward science, and already he had a good grounding in botany. In the early 1700's, medicine and botany went hand in hand; the recognized drugs for the various illnesses were herbs and other plants. It was essential that a medical man also be something of a botanist. Rothman talked with Carl and stimulated his interest in a physician's career. But since the boy knew that his parents were determined he should be a clergyman he begged Lannerus and Rothman not to speak to his family of his longing for a different future.

At length, toward the end of Carl's period at Växjö, Nils Linnaeus had occasion to go to the town to consult

Dr. Rothman about his health. At the same time, he took the opportunity to inquire of the Växjö teachers about Carl's progress. Their response stunned him. Carl was reported to be an indifferent, careless, almost hopeless scholar, and Nils was advised to take him out of school and apprentice him to a craftsman of some kind — possibly a carpenter or a shoemaker. In deep shock, Nils went on to Rothman's house. There he asked the doctor's opinion not only of his own health, but also of Carl's future.

Rothman was comforting. He took an entirely different view of Carl from that of the other Växjö teachers. It was true, he said, that the boy would never make a satisfactory clergyman, but he did show promise in other fields. Rothman suggested a medical career for Carl. He went even further than that. If Nils did not feel he could bear the cost of keeping his son at Växjö, Rothman said, he would take the boy into his own home and give him private instruction for a year, until he was old enough to enter a university.

Nils had doubts about the whole idea. He dreaded his wife's disappointment. Her mind was set on Carl's being a clergyman. Besides this, Nils knew that a doctor's training would be expensive. There were younger children in the family now, and he could not be sure of paying Carl's way much longer.

Finally he agreed to Rothman's plan in some measure. For the next year, Carl had some private instruction from the doctor. Rothman took great pains with his pupil. Not only did he teach Carl physiology, but also he allowed the boy to use his library, and he saw to it that Carl read widely in the field of botany. By this means, Carl Linnaeus became acquainted with the work of Joseph Pitton de Tournefort (1656-1708), a French botanist who had worked out a system of placing plants into various groups according to the form of their flowers and fruits. At the time, this was the most modern and complete system of plant classification there was, and it appealed to Carl's orderly mind. He liked to put his learning into categories. He spent many hours restudying the local plants and grouping them according to Tournefort's methods.

Even more important to Carl's botanical future was Rothman's mentioning to him the theories of the French botanist Sébastien Vaillant (1669-1722). During his years of close observation of the structure of plants, Vaillant had noted the male and female parts that were important in plant reproduction; he died before he could fully develop his ideas about them. While similar ideas had been put forth by some of the ancients and had been rediscovered by more recent botanists, theories about sex in plants were considered somewhat startling by many of Vaillant's contemporaries. In a searching mind like that of young Carl Linnaeus, however, Vaillant's theories could not help but raise questions.

Young Carl's year under Rothman's tutoring left him

abuzz with many new thoughts. He spent the summer with his family at Stenbrohult. There he worked mightily to group the plants — the old friends of his childhood — according to the Tournefort method of classification that he had learned. He did not always succeed. Perhaps even then he perceived how unwieldy Tournefort's system could be.

After much argument he finally succeeded in convincing his father that he should study to be a physician and a botanist, although his mother still bitterly opposed the plan. In the fall he was to enter the university at Lund, in the province of Skåne. Here an old friend of the family, Dean Humerus, was attached to the cathedral, and it was hoped that he might be of help to young Carl.

THE YEAR AT LUND

LUND AND ITS UNIVERSITY PROVED A GRAVE
disappointment to Linnaeus.

At that time, Lund was a little market center
surrounded by outlying farms. On its one long
main street stood the cathedral, with the larger
houses of the town clustered about it. Away
from this one thoroughfare, narrow paths led to
the less important dwellings of the community.
Farm animals roamed wherever they liked, and

dead animals occasionally lay in the dirt and mud of the long street for days, without anyone's seeming to care. The whole scene was disheartening, especially to a newcomer. To make matters worse, Linnaeus soon learned that Dean Humerus had recently died. So the would-be student found himself without guidance in a strange and rather unattractive place.

Fortunately Gabriel Höök, who had been Carl's tutor for a short time in his grammar school days, was now a Master of Philosophy at Lund. Linnaeus turned to him for information about entering the university, and Höök was able to help him. On August 19, 1727, Carl Linnaeus was formally enrolled as a student at Lund, at the age of twenty.

The university students lived in the homes of the community and from these quarters went to listen to the lectures of the professors they wished to hear. Höök found lodging for Linnaeus with Dr. Kilian Stobaeus, a man who was well respected both for his medical skill and his knowledge of natural history.

Now Linnaeus had a further disappointment. He had come to Lund with high hopes of finding good instruction both in botany and medicine. But, though the university did have some able professors, no one at all was lecturing on botany at this time. Moreover, medical instruction was of the scantiest kind. There was one professor of medicine, but he was badly handicapped for lack of material to illustrate his lectures on anatomy and other subjects. Linnaeus attended what medical lectures were given, but they helped him very little.

Lund did have a good university library, and Linnaeus used it to launch himself on a program of self-education. He quickly became familiar with the natural history books in the library collection.

He was also fortunate in being quartered in the home of Stobaeus, though at first the doctor had little liking for the young student. In his autobiography, Linnaeus later described Stobaeus as an ailing, one-eyed man with a crippled foot — a man constantly dogged by migraine and backache — but at the same time a genius. In addition to his other troubles, Stobaeus was sadly overworked, and had little time for pleasantries. Linnaeus made a poor first impression when he was asked by the doctor to help him by writing a letter in answer to some questions from a patient about an illness. Linnaeus' handwriting proved to be so bad that the letter had to be discarded as worthless.

While Linnaeus and the doctor may at first have had doubts about each other, the young student was greatly impressed with Stobaeus' excellent library and with the natural history museum the doctor had made of the birds, plants, rocks, and shells he had collected. In his autobiography, Linnaeus tells of the events that finally led to a cordial liking between the doctor and himself.

Stobaeus had a secretary, a German medical student named Koulas, who was allowed to use the doctor's library freely — something Linnaeus was not permitted to do. Young Linnaeus made a bargain with Koulas, offering to teach him all the physiology he himself had learned from Dr. Rothman. In return, Koulas was to lend Linnaeus books from Stobaeus' library each night — among them many valuable books on botany. They could be returned early in the morning without the doctor's ever being aware of the arrangement.

Koulas agreed, and the plan worked perfectly for a while. But then Stobaeus' mother, old and unable to sleep, began to take notice of the nightly crack of light under Linnaeus' door, into the late hours when the rest of the house was in darkness. In those days of candlelight and wooden dwellings an outbreak of fire was an ever present danger. The old lady was sure that Linnaeus must carelessly leave his candle burning while he slept, and she feared a conflagration.

When Stobaeus learned of the light he lost no time in visiting Linnaeus' room late at night. Expecting to find the young man asleep and to awaken him and give him a scolding, the doctor entered the room quietly. Much to his surprise, Linnaeus sat at his table, surrounded by books from Stobaeus' own library.

When the doctor had heard Linnaeus' explanation, he ordered the midnight student to put out his candle and go to bed at once. The next morning, Stobaeus talked with Linnaeus and ended by giving him a key to the library. From then on, Carl was allowed to use the doctor's books as often as he wished.

Soon a warm friendship grew between Dr. Stobaeus and Linnaeus. Even though the university might be lacking in medical lectures, the young student gained much from his constant association with the older man. The doctor allowed Linnaeus to go with him on visits to his patients; he talked with him for hours about the science of the day; he even provided him with free board. Once again, Carl Linnaeus had found a friend in time of crisis.

In Stobaeus' home, Linnaeus saw for the first time a well-arranged natural history collection. He was especially pleased by Stobaeus' herbarium, a series of dried plants carefully pressed and mounted on separate sheets of paper and each neatly labeled by name. This was the first such plant collection Linnaeus had seen, and he immediately started an herbarium of his own.

Once again, as he had at Växjö, he went out into the fields, but now his excursions covered much more territory. Because Lund was fairly near the coast, he became acquainted with the plants in the salt marshes and meadows, and with marine plants.

At Lund he found plants strange to him, and he discovered that the ones he had known so well in Stenbrohult did not grow here. The soil and the whole countryside were different. Lund was flat, with clayey soil and few forests; Stenbrohult was in rolling country, heavily wooded. Linnaeus quickly realized that the differences in the lay of the land and in the soil influenced the plant life of the area.

Reading in the libraries, searching the neighboring districts for new plant specimens, talking with Stobaeus — all these activities sharpened Linnaeus' perceptions of plants and their similarities and differences. So did the work of making an herbarium. As Linnaeus pressed, dried, and mounted his specimens he had a chance to observe them more closely. Once they were mounted, he could go back to them again and again, examining even the smallest details of their leaves and flowers, comparing them with other plants, and trying to use Tournefort's method of classifying them.

During one of his botany trips, Linnaeus was stung or bitten on the arm by an animal of some kind — he was never quite sure what. A bad infection followed and he almost lost his life. When he recovered he went home to Stenbrohult for the summer. Here Dr. Rothman visited him. Upon hearing of Linnaeus' disappointment with the university at Lund, Rothman urged him to change to that at Uppsala, also in Sweden. Rothman had attended Uppsala years before, and remembered its very fine library, its beautiful botanical garden, and its distinguished lecturers — Professor Lars Roberg in medicine, and Professor Olof Rudbeck in botany. All these assets would work to the advantage of a young student like Linnaeus, Rothman was sure.

Carl Linnaeus agreed, but there was the difficult question of money. Nils Linnaeus now had four children younger than Carl, and he could no longer afford to pay his eldest son's expenses at the university. Dr. Rothman had said that at Uppsala there were some royal scholarships which a good student might earn, but that did not help for the present. Nils Linnaeus did manage to scrape together a final sum for Carl — about fifty dollars — and on August 23, 1728, at the age of twenty-one, Carl Linnaeus set off for the university at Uppsala, to make his own way from then on.

A STUDENT AT UPPSALA

JUST AS AT LUND, LINNAEUS WAS FACED WITH
bitter disappointment at Uppsala. The university
was far different from the splendid place that Dr.
Rothman remembered from his student days. A
dreadful fire had swept Uppsala in 1702, scorch-
ing the botanical garden and destroying its greenhouses as well as burning down the greater part
of the town. The damage had never been completely repaired.

Moreover, while both Roberg and Rudbeck still held professorships in the university, they were aging men and their energies had flagged. Roberg, at sixty-five, was responsible for teaching medicine, physiology, and chemistry, but he found this schedule rather too strenuous. Besides, he had become greedy for money. He had given up almost all his lecturing except to private pupils, who paid well for the privilege of listening to him. The poorer students, who would have benefited by the public lectures Roberg had given in the past, were forced to go without instruction.

In his day, Olof Rudbeck had been a great lecturer on botany and zoology. Linnaeus had looked forward eagerly to hearing him and watching him demonstrate his talks with the wealth of materials he had gathered in his scientific travels. But Rudbeck was now sixty-eight and had been greatly disheartened by a grievous loss during the fire of 1702. Some years before that, in 1695, Rudbeck and his father had been commissioned by King Charles XI to explore Sweden's northern territory of Lapland and report on its plants. After their return the father and son had labored for some years in writing a great work, illustrated with beautifully made woodcuts of the plants they had found in Lapland. But in the fire that ruined Uppsala the volumes already printed had been destroyed within a few hours, together with the notes for further work and thousands of woodcuts already made.

A Student at Uppsala

The elder Rudbeck never recovered from the blow, and died a few months later. His son, short of money, lacked the courage or will power to begin the great project again. Instead, he turned to writing a monumental book on languages — a subject he also knew well. When Linnaeus arrived at Uppsala, Olof Rudbeck was still occupied with this work and was on leave of absence from his regular position. He gave only a very few lectures each year.

It is no wonder that Linnaeus felt downhearted. To him it seemed as if he could not have chosen a worse place to come for a medical education. Not only were the two famous lecturers Roberg and Rudbeck all but silent and the botanical garden in ruins, but also the hospital where the medical students might have received some clinical instruction was in terrible disrepair. There was so little money to maintain it that Roberg was forced to let out some of its rooms as a beerhouse.

Moreover, there was no opportunity for medical students to visit patients in their homes; no anatomy was taught at all; no chemical laboratory existed. Chemical demonstrations were occasionally given at the university apothecary's, but the experiments shown were of the simplest kind.

In addition, Carl Linnaeus was plagued by terrible poverty. Soon the money his father had given him was gone — paid out for lodging, food, and other expenses. He could find no work to do, as the career of medicine was in low standing at the time, and medical students were considered unworthy of hiring for the various jobs that might have given them an income. Linnaeus was forced to borrow money for food, and he ate poorly, often going hungry. His shoes wore out and he patched them with folded paper and placed layers of paper inside them to cover the holes in the soles.

He did manage to attend a few of Roberg's private lectures, and he heard Rudbeck lecture on birds. As he talked, Rudbeck showed the accurate and glowing colored drawings that he and some of his students had made on a zoological expedition to Lapland. To Linnaeus, with his memories of the sunny Stenbrohult meadows of his childhood, it was a thrilling experience to see these lovely pictures.

During the rest of the first term at Uppsala, Linnaeus kept busy with his program of self-education. Dr. Rothman had spoken truly of the university's fine library and soon Linnaeus was deep in the books on natural science. Among other treasures the library had a large collection of dried plants — a collection that Linnaeus studied constantly. In December he was awarded a small royal scholarship, and because of this income the days looked brighter.

In spring of the next year, 1729, things looked brighter yet, for two pieces of good fortune came to Linnaeus. First, he made a close friend of his own age, Peter Artedi, also a student at Uppsala. In Linnaeus' early days at the university various people had spoken to him of Artedi, because the two young men seemed to have much in common. Both had been theology students who had turned to the natural sciences as their true field. In addition, Artedi was a keen chemistry student — apparently the only one at the university.

But during Linnaeus' first term, Artedi had been at home because of his father's serious illness. Now, in March, 1729, Artedi returned. His father had died, and the son was pale and downcast. Linnaeus, hearing that Artedi had come back, hurried to meet him. The two were instantly attracted to each other, different though they were in appearance and temperament. Artedi was tall and thin and handsome, slow to form an opinion, and deeply earnest. Linnaeus was small and darting, hasty to anger and laughter, and quick-witted.

Almost at once their talk turned to the things of natural science: minerals, plants, animals. In Artedi, Linnaeus recognized a natural scientist as ardent as himself. Much that Artedi said was new to Linnaeus, and he was astonished and fascinated by it.

Soon the two students were meeting every day to exchange the thoughts and information that had come to them in the hours since they had last seen each other. A certain rivalry existed between them at first, and sometimes they made an effort to keep their new discoveries to themselves. But both of them were eager and enthusiastic, and their minds were churning with ideas. Besides, theirs was a warm and affectionate friendship. Keeping silent was impossible. Before long, in spite of their resolves, they found themselves talking freely and sharing even their deepest secrets.

It soon became evident that each had special subjects in which he excelled, and looking ahead, they planned their futures with this in mind. They decided to divide the field of natural science between themselves. Each would become an authority in certain things. Artedi loved chemistry and fishes and the amphibia, the last of which Linnaeus disliked intensely. Plants, birds, and insects belonged to Linnaeus. Now each reported his daily progress in his own fields; they shared the subjects of mammals and mineralogy.

Linnaeus' second piece of good fortune came about by chance — but a chance that might have had no consequences at all for a person less botanically learned than himself. As it was, it turned out to be an important event in the shaping of his career. It happened this way.

One spring day in 1729, Linnaeus was sitting in the university garden, examining some plants and writing descriptions of what he found. Even though the garden was sadly run down, some interesting plant specimens still remained. As Linnaeus worked, a stranger dressed in a clergyman's habit entered the garden. Upon seeing Linnaeus, the man began to question him about the plants he was examining. Did he know their names? Had he studied botany? Where had he come from? How long had he been at the university?

The clergyman, his interest apparently quickened by the answers he received, then went on to ask Linnaeus the names of a number of plants that he pointed out. Linnaeus named them all according to Tournefort's method of classification.

Next, the clergyman inquired if Linnaeus had a plant collection of his own. Carl answered that he had gathered and pressed about six hundred of the native plants of Sweden. At this, the gentleman invited Linnaeus to go with him to his home.

Linnaeus was flabbergasted when the two turned in at the dwelling of Dr. Olaf Celsius. Celsius was an eminent man — a professor of theology at the university and also a dean of the cathedral. Carl had heard of him often but had never seen him before, as Celsius had been on a long sojourn in Stockholm and had just returned. Besides his theological interests, Celsius was an enthusiastic student of natural history and had a special love of plants.

Celsius talked further with Linnaeus and apparently liked him and found him knowledgeable in botany. Several days later, after he had examined Linnaeus' herbarium and had also noticed that Linnaeus had little money, Celsius gave the young man a room in his house. Linnaeus ate many of his meals there and became almost a member of the family. Once again, a benefactor had appeared at the right moment.

At this time, Olaf Celsius was preparing a book, *Hierobotanican,* on the plants of the Bible. Linnaeus was able to help him in this enterprise. He plunged into the project vigorously, bringing all his botanical knowledge and youthful energy to the task. Working with Celsius on the writing of this book was one of the best experiences young Linnaeus could have had at this time. In the course of the project he learned much about the preparation of a botanical manuscript — something that was soon to prove useful to him.

In addition to his knowledge of the plants of the Bible, Celsius was an authority on the plants of Upland, the province in which Uppsala lay. He inspired Linnaeus to hunt out plant specimens for miles around, and often Celsius and Linnaeus went on long expeditions together. Linnaeus benefited by the older man's close acquaintance with the plant life of the area and he found the clergyman a good companion as well.

Celsius had one of the finest libraries in Sweden — a library rich in botanical books. Here, once again, Linnaeus found mention of the French botanist Vaillant and his work on the structure of flowers and the sexual characteristics of plants. Ever since his Växjö days with Rothman, knowledge of Vaillant's ideas had lain in the back of Linnaeus' mind. He must have had glimmerings of these ideas often as he strode through the fields, stopping now and then to pick a strange flower and hold it close to examine its structure.

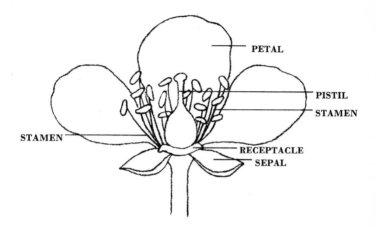

Cross section drawing, showing the parts of a flower. Here the stamens and the pistil occur in the same flower. The pistil, the female reproductive organ, is in the center of the flower; the stamens, male organs, are grouped around it.

In Celsius' library, as he read of Vaillant again, Linnaeus' thoughts came into focus. He was older now — a more experienced and perceptive botanist — and his companionship with Artedi and Celsius had made him alert to the strange possibilities in nature. With Vaillant's views in mind, Linnaeus began to look at his plant specimens even more closely. Slowly what had before been only an idea became reality to him.

There was no doubt that flowering plants grew from seeds. And seeds never formed unless there were flowers first. Moreover, certain parts of a flower seemed to be important in seed-making. There were the stamens, which Vaillant and others claimed were the male parts of the flower, and the pistils, which were the female parts. Linnaeus became convinced that the stamens and the pistils were the sexual organs and that they played the important role in the reproduction of flowering plants. In order to increase their own kind, flowering plants needed male and female parents, just as animals did.

Although, at the time, this was a novel idea to the public at large, it was by no means a new idea to natural scientists. Aristotle (384-322 B.C.), a great Greek philosopher and scientific investigator, had been aware that plants were divided into male and female, and that if pollen from the male parts were shaken on the female parts, seeds would form. Theophrastus (372-287 B.C.), also a Greek philosopher and a natural historian, and

A Student at Uppsala

Pliny the Elder (A.D. 23-79), a famous Roman natural historian, knew of the sexuality of plants, as did the later botanists Nehemiah Grew (1641-1712), Rudolf Jakob Camerarius (1665-1721), John Ray (1627-1705), and others. Vaillant was the botanist who influenced Linnaeus, however, for it was Vaillant's writings that he was aware of at this time.

Whatever other work had been done in the field, it remained for Linnaeus to discuss the sexuality of plants clearly and in detail and to show how generally it occurred. The subject of sex in plants had begun to arouse definite interest in Uppsala even before Linnaeus made himself heard. In December, 1729, the university librarian, Georg Wallin, led a debate, *De Nuptiis Arborum,* or "Concerning the Marriage of Trees." Linnaeus did not agree with the views there expressed, but for some reason was unable to dispute them at the time.

Instead, he wrote out what he considered the correct views on sex in plants and presented his little dissertation to Olaf Celsius as a New Year's greeting. Today it seems a strange one. In those days, though, students usually composed poems to their professors and presented them at the beginning of a new year. To Linnaeus, whose whole life centered around green growing things, a greeting that dealt with reproduction in plants seemed far superior to a poem. To him, there was nothing odd about it.

Nor, apparently, did Celsius find it odd. He was delighted — and much impressed. Even today a reader can sense the infinite study and pondering and the painstaking care that the twenty-two-year-old student put into the work. This is no amateur effort. It is well reasoned, with quotations from many learned authorities, and it is well written.

True, it was science. But Linnaeus had a streak of romance and poetry in his nature. He could not write — or even think — of such a beloved subject as plants in dull, dry, scientific terms alone. He began his treatise in a most romantic way, with springtime. Then, he said, all living things awaken, after having lain quiet during the winter, and they grow lively and active. The birds chirp and sing, the insects appear, the plants spring up, and the trees burst into leaf. The sun brings joy to all the animals, and it is then that they mate. Even the plants are seized by an urge to mate. Linnaeus then went on to compare plants with animals; to explain the structure of the flowers; and to show that the stamens and the pistils are the main organs of reproduction.

His treatise created quite a stir in Uppsala. Manuscript copies of it were circulated among the students; the Uppsala Scientific Society showed an interest in printing it; there was much discussion of it. Professor Olof Rudbeck, on seeing a copy, was immediately interested. Which of Celsius' students, he asked the clergyman, was so well grounded in botany as to write such a work? He would be most pleased to meet the young man.

A Student at Uppsala

As it happened, Rudbeck at this time was looking for someone to give the botany lectures in the university garden at the end of each spring term. He was still busy with his work on languages, and the university had allowed him some money to hire a substitute lecturer. At first he had thought of a young man named Preutz, but after taking him into the garden and questioning him about the plants, Rudbeck had decided that Preutz was not well enough acquainted with them.

Thereupon he sent for Linnaeus and took him into the botanical garden. After questioning him thoroughly and examining his knowledge of the plants, Rudbeck finally asked Linnaeus if he would undertake the lectures. Linnaeus was completely astonished, as he was only a student himself. He agreed to try, however, if Rudbeck would trust him. Professor Roberg protested violently at having so young a man take such a responsible position, but Rudbeck insisted. On May 4, 1730, Linnaeus gave his first lecture in the Uppsala botanical garden.

Naturally the other students were curious about this young man who had written the paper on plants and had caused so much talk — and who now had stepped into the shoes of Professor Rudbeck. Between two and three hundred listeners crowded the garden to hear Linnaeus give his first lecture on the plants that could be found there. He was an instant success. Actually the lectures were much like those that Rudbeck had given. They stated the names of the plants, dwelt heavily on their uses for medicinal purposes, told a few interesting anecdotes about each plant specimen, and quoted from classical writers. But Linnaeus was a born lecturer and teacher. His voice was pleasing; his eyes sparkled and his face lit up when he talked. His burning enthusiasm for his subject fired the members of his audience and carried them along with him. For the rest of the term his lectures continued to be popular. Rudbeck was well pleased.

Rudbeck was so well pleased, in fact, that in June he asked Linnaeus to live in his house and become the tutor for three of his younger sons. In addition, Linnaeus was to coach one of the older boys in medicine. (Rudbeck had been married three times and had twenty-four children.)

For his work, Linnaeus received a small salary. At about the same time, Rudbeck made a request to the proper authorities to have Linnaeus' royal scholarship increased, because he was "one of the most spirited and promising young men folk" at the university. The request was granted, and suddenly Linnaeus was a young man with an adequate income. He was able to pay off his debts and no longer had to worry about such lowly things as mending his shoes.

In addition, Linnaeus took on some private pupils in botany. Some of them paid him in money, some in books, and some in such useful articles as hats, gloves, stockings, purses — whatever extra things they might own.

Linnaeus' accounting of the payments from his students still exists. Somehow the young men who studied with Linnaeus over two hundred years ago seem very much alive when we read that one of them paid his tutor a wig for his lesson, and another paid "one fine button stud" and, on another day, "one toothpick."

Olof Rudbeck lived in a spacious house next to the botanical garden — a location that Linnaeus found most convenient. Rudbeck, too, had a fine library, which Linnaeus was free to use. The young man profited also from the conversation and advice of Rudbeck, a kindly man who was generous with the learning he had acquired during a lifetime of experience with plants and animals.

Stimulated by his sudden success and by his fortunate surroundings, Linnaeus threw himself into a tornado of activity. During the day he lectured or attended to the lessons of the Rudbeck boys or his private pupils. At night he worked on his own ideas.

In examining plants to learn more about their stamens and pistils, he had noticed that in some different kinds of plants these parts were as unlike each other — especially in number and proportion — as the petals were. For example, he found that some kinds of flowers always had only one stamen; some kinds had two stamens; some had three. Some kinds of flowers had four stamens, all more or less the same length; some had four stamens, two of which were always longer than the others. There were many other differences in the number and length

41

of stamens among the kinds of flowers, and there were differences in the way the stamens grew. Some always grew as separate stalks within the flower, while others in a different kind of flower were always joined together in some way. There were even stranger differences, too. Often the stamens (the male parts) and the pistils (the female parts) grew in the same flower, but not always. Sometimes the stamens and pistils grew in separate flowers on the same plant; sometimes they grew not only in separate flowers but on separate plants as well.

Hitherto, plants had most often been classified into groups according to the similarities of their flowers or fruits. Tournefort's method of classifying plants had been according to their flower and fruit forms. But as Linnaeus studied his plant specimens, pondering them, arranging and rearranging them into groups, he began to doubt that Tournefort's was a satisfactory system. Peter Artedi had been thinking of making a new classification of the *Umbelliferae,* a group of plants with umbrella-shaped blossoms. Now Linnaeus wondered if a new arrangement of all plants might not be an idea to work on. Vaillant had hinted at the possibility of grouping together plants whose flowers had like stamens or pistils. Why not try such a new system, ignoring Tournefort's arrangement entirely and putting the plants into altogether different groupings?

Such a project appealed mightily to Linnaeus, with his love of order. He once described himself as "a born methodizer." Now all his thoughts were bent on a new

A Student at Uppsala

The City of Uppsala.

method of arranging the known plants into groups. To him this was an exciting venture — too secret even to confide to Artedi. He resolved to study and describe accurately all the flowers he knew, putting them into the new classes he would decide on, and even changing the names of the plants when necessary.

At the same time, Linnaeus was working on another project that was the direct result of his lectures in the botanical garden. His students had asked him to draw up a catalog of the plants he included in his lectures. Such a list would be a great aid to his listeners as, when he named the plants, they could turn to them quickly in the catalog instead of trying to copy each name down hastily as it was mentioned — and probably spelling it wrong in the process. In response to this request, Linnaeus drew up the catalog, called *Hortus Uplandica* (*An Upland Garden*). This was afterward revised and enlarged many times.

At first, Linnaeus used Tournefort's system for grouping the plants in his catalog, but as early as July, 1730, he began to arrange them according to a plan of his own. As the various revisions of the catalog came out from that time on, small improvements and changes in plant names were made. Even at that early date, Linnaeus had begun planning the system of plant classification that in a few years was to make him famous.

At the same time, he had thought out and begun the writing of various other works of botany and zoology. In Rudbeck's house he had the opportunity to study carefully Rudbeck's beautiful drawings of Swedish birds. They inspired Linnaeus to draw up a new classification of the native birds as well as one of insects. Linnaeus was a tireless worker on things that interested him, and he liked to make every minute count. These were busy days and nights for the earnest young student.

Linnaeus lived in the Rudbeck household for eighteen months. In July, 1731, at the end of the midsummer term, he journeyed to Stockholm with one of his private pupils, Carl Gustaf Warmholtz. Warmholtz' father was an apothecary, and in Stockholm Linnaeus took the opportunity to learn something of pharmacy from his host, as well as to visit the gardens of the vicinity and study the natural science collection at the College of Medicine.

By the end of July he was back in Uppsala. A change in his fortunes had come about, however. Some time before this, Nils Rosén, a brilliant medical student, had returned to Uppsala from his travels abroad. When Rudbeck had been granted a leave of absence from his lectures, the medical faculty and the chancellor of the university had agreed that as soon as Rosén returned from his long journey and had been graduated, he should be appointed adjunct, or assistant, to Rudbeck and should take over Rudbeck's duties. During the spring term of 1731, Rosén had lectured on anatomy in place of Rudbeck, while Linnaeus had continued the botany lectures.

In this second year of lecturing, Linnaeus had improved the botanical garden, rearranging it according to his own plan, and he had managed to obtain many rare plants for it. In addition, he had extended the scope of his talks. His future as a botanical lecturer looked promising. But now Rosén wished to take over the botanical lectures. This was a severe blow to Linnaeus, and a move that he bitterly resented, but there was nothing he could do to forestall Rosén, who was clearly acting within his rights.

Rudbeck had often talked to Linnaeus about his journey to Lapland years before, and Linnaeus had pored over Rudbeck's lovely drawings of the Lapland birds. For some time, Linnaeus had felt a longing to see this largely unexplored land which presented such a new and challenging field to a young student of natural history. Now, with his future at Uppsala somewhat in doubt, he was more eager than ever to make the Lapland journey.

In December, 1731, he returned to Stenbrohult to stay with his family. But before he left the university he wrote to the Scientific Society at Uppsala, presenting his plan to explore Lapland, and asking them to finance the journey. The society had funds to make it possible for its members to investigate the natural resources of Swedish territory or to send other persons to do this work.

In his document to the Scientific Society, Linnaeus listed the qualifications that he felt any explorer of Lapland in his day should have. He wrote:

"He should be

"A. A native of Sweden.

"B. Young and in good condition, so that he may travel with ease over the steep hills and into the deep valleys.

"C. Healthy, so that he may make the journey more easily.

"D. Tireless even in difficulties, for he may find himself short of food; he must be on foot, stooping, and suffering heat and thirst and many difficulties, since this is no pleasure trip for a pampered gentleman.

"E. Without other duties, for this trip requires his highest duty.

"F. Unmarried, so that he may risk his life on the waters of the rivers, etc., without thinking of the possibility of leaving his children fatherless.

"G. Skilled in the fundamentals of natural history and medicine, so that he may bring better insight to his task.

"H. Understanding in all three kingdoms of nature; this is perhaps more difficult to find than a bird of paradise, for there are few botanists who know the other two kingdoms thoroughly, and there is almost none who is competent in all.

"I. A born naturalist, not one that has been made, for it is remarkable how different they are in accomplishment.

"J. A draftsman, so that he can draw the things he observes, and so describe them better."

Linnaeus went on to say that few men in Sweden had all the qualifications necessary for making the trip and that, failing a better candidate, he would suggest himself as the Lapland traveler.

In Stenbrohult there was a long wait for an answer to his suggestion, and in April he sent the members of the Scientific Society another outline of his project, to jog their memories. In the meantime, there was a happy stay at home as Linnaeus told of his university life, became reacquainted with his younger brother and three sisters, walked in the fields and woods he had known so well in his younger years, worked at his writing, and talked of his future plans. In February, 1732, he paid a thirteen-day visit to his dear friend Dr. Stobaeus at Lund.

His plans for the Lapland journey created a sensation at home — but not a pleasant one. They were highly disapproved of by his parents. To them, the trip seemed like the most harebrained of ventures, and dangerous besides. But finally Nils Linnaeus accepted the inevitable and commended his son to God's care, saying, "He is everywhere, even in the wildest mountains. Trust in Him!"

At last, March came and spring began to make a reluctant appearance. At the first sign of thaw, Linnaeus was off to Uppsala, to await the Scientific Society's hoped-for approval of his trip. It finally came on April 15, 1732. But Lapland is far north, and the weather was still too cold for starting the journey. Linnaeus spent the time before his departure in a visit to Stockholm, in writing, in conversation with his friends, and in making preparations for the trip.

The Scientific Society had not granted Linnaeus much money, and because of the rough country he would be obliged either to walk or to travel by horseback or small boat. His preparations, then, were necessarily simple and he planned to carry no more equipment than was absolutely essential.

Before he left, he had one particularly difficult farewell to say — to Peter Artedi, who was going to study in England. Artedi and Linnaeus reminded each other of their division of thé fields of natural history, and each pledged that if anything fatal should happen to the other, the survivor would see that his friend's writings were published.

At last the weather grew warmer, and finally the long-awaited day of departure came. On May 12, 1732, Carl Linnaeus said good-bye to his friends and rode out the northern gate of Uppsala, bound for Lapland and the greatest adventure of his life. (Dates for his journey accord with the old-style Swedish calendar.)

THE LAPLAND JOURNEY

TO LINNAEUS, RIDING NORTHWARD ON THAT
May morning in 1732, it seemed that all the
world smiled. The sun shone; the weather was
warm; the spring fields were softly green. He was
young and footloose — "within half a day of
twenty-five years of age." The long winter routine
of work lay behind him. He was up and away,
and traveling light.

His original journal, handwritten in Swedish

and Latin as he went along, and illustrated with his own rough drawings of what he observed, may still be seen at the Linnean Society in London. It has been translated by James Edward Smith as *A Tour of Lapland*. In it, Linnaeus described himself as he started on his journey.

"[I wore] a light coat of linsey-woolsey cloth without folds, lined with red shalloon, having small cuffs and collar of shag; leather breeches; a round wig; a green leather cap, and a pair of half boots. I carried a small leather bag, half an ell in length, but somewhat less in breadth, furnished on one side with hooks and eyes, so that it could be opened and shut at pleasure. This bag contained one shirt, two pairs of false sleeves; two half shirts; an inkstand, pencase, microscope, and spyglass; a gauze cap to protect me occasionally from the gnats; a comb; my journal, and a parcel of paper stitched together for drying plants, both in folio; my manuscripts *Ornithology, Flora Uplandica,* and *Characteres Generica.* I wore a hanger at my side, and carried a small fowling piece, as well as an eight-sided stick, marked off for the purpose of measuring. My pocketbook contained a passport from the governor of Uppsala, and a recommendation from the Royal Academy of Sciences."

The road led through pleasant country. "Uppsala for the distance of a quarter of a mile [a Swedish mile was the equal of about six English miles] is surrounded with fertile cornfields which are bounded by hills, and the view is terminated by spacious forests.

"Now the winter corn was half a foot in height, and the barley had just shot out its blade. The birch, the alder, and the aspen tree began to put forth their leaves. . . . The lark was my companion all the way, flying before me, quivering in the air.

"Okstad is a mile and a quarter from Uppsala. Here the forests began to thicken. The charming lark, which had till now attended my steps, here left me; but another bird welcomed my approach to the forest, the redwing . . . whose amorous warblings from the tops of the spruce fir were no less delightful. Its lofty and varied notes rival those of the nightingale herself."

Even though Linnaeus rode on horseback, his sharp eyes missed not even the smallest flowers and he alighted often to examine them more closely. On May 13 he writes of the hepatica and wood sorrel growing along the way. Rain threatened and "their blossoms were all closed. Who has endowed plants with intelligence, to shut themselves up at the approach of rain? Even when the weather changes in a moment from sunshine to rain, though before expanded, they immediately close. Here for the first time this season I heard the cuckoo, a welcome harbinger of summer."

On May 15 he noted: "The spiders had now spread their curious mathematical webs over the pales and fences, and they were rendered conspicuous by the moisture with which the fog besprinkled them. The redwing, the cuckoo, the black grouse, and the mountain finch with their various notes made a concert in the forest, to which the lowing herds of cattle under the shade of the trees formed a bass. The weather this morning was delightfully pleasant."

But he was traveling steadily northward, and the flowers gradually disappeared from along his path. By May 20 he found the country covered with snow. Nothing but wintry plants — the heath and the whortleberry — peeped through the icy drifts. Even so, there was some brightness in this northern land. On May 25 he wrote, "In the cornfields lay hundreds of gulls of a sky-blue color."

He had traveled through the provinces of Gävle, Gästrikland, Hälsingland, Medelpad, and Ångermanland, and at length arrived at Umeå, in the province of Västerbotten. At Umeå he visited the governor of the province, a courteous man who entertained his guest by showing him his pets — crossbills in a birdcage, and a tame otter that had become so accustomed to a domestic way of life that it refused to go into the water or to eat live fish.

On May 26, Linnaeus left Umeå. "The weather was rainy, and continued so during the day. I turned out of the main road to the left, my design being to visit Lycksele Lappmark. By this means I missed the advantage I had hitherto had at the regular posthouses, of commanding a horse whenever I pleased; which is no small convenience to a stranger traveling in Sweden. It now became necessary for me to entreat in the most submissive manner when I stood in need of this useful animal. The road grew more and more narrow and bad, so that my horse went stumbling along at almost every step, among stones, at the hazard of my life. My path was so narrow and intricate, along so many byways, that nothing human could have followed my track. In this dreary wilderness I began to feel very solitary, and to long earnestly for a companion."

In the evening he came upon some women cutting aspen bark into shreds to be used as fodder for cows, goats, and sheep. Hay was very scarce in this part of the country. Linnaeus stopped to see if he could get food for his supper, and the women set before him the breast of a woodcock that had been shot and prepared the year before. It looked so uninviting that Linnaeus dreaded the taste. To his surprise it was delicious. He describes in his journal exactly how it had been salted and dried.

Rain came down so violently that he could not continue his journey after supper and was obliged to spend the night at this same spot. "The pillows of my bed were stuffed with the hair of the reindeer instead of feathers. Under the sheet was the hide of a reindeer with the hair on, the hairy side uppermost, on which the people told me I should lie very soft."

The next day, May 27, he wrote, "At noon I departed from the place where I had slept, and continued to pursue the same bad road as the preceding day, which was indeed the worst I ever saw, consisting of stones piled on stones, among large entangled roots of trees. In the interstices were deep holes filled with water by the heavy rains. The frost, which had just left the ground, contributed to make matters worse. All the elements were against me. The branches of the trees hung down over my eyes, loaded with raindrops, in every direction. Wherever any young birch trees appeared, they were bent down to the earth so that they could not be passed without the greatest difficulty. The aged pines, which for so many seasons had raised their proud tops above the rest of the forest, overthrown by the wrath of Juno, lay prostrate in my way. The rivulets which traversed the country in various directions were very deep, and the bridges over them so decayed and ruinous that it was at the peril of one's neck to pass them on a stumbling horse. . . .

"Many persons had confidently assured me that it was absolutely impossible to travel to Lycksele in the summer season; but I had always comforted myself with the saying of Solomon, that 'nothing is impossible under the sun.' However, I found that if patience be requisite anywhere, it is at this place. To complete my distresses, I had just got a horse whose saddle was not stuffed, and instead of a bridle I had only a rope, which was tied to the animal's underjaw. In this trim I proceeded on my journey."

Drawing from Linnaeus' journal of his Lapland travels: Lapp carrying his boat over his head.

But even under these uncomfortable circumstances, Linnaeus was his usual observant self. "As a protection against rain, the people wear a broad horizontal collar made of birch bark, fastened around the neck with pins.

"The women wash their houses with a kind of brush, made of twigs of spruce fir, which they tie to the right foot and go backward and forward over the floor."

On May 28, Linnaeus came to Genom. From there the only means of getting to Lycksele was by boat. He had not arrived at Genom until nine o'clock in the evening, and the wind was blowing so hard that he decided to stay overnight. A man in the neighborhood had shot a beaver, and Linnaeus took the opportunity to examine it.

The next morning, May 29, he set out with a guide for Lycksele. As the boat hastened along, Linnaeus noted the birds: ringed plovers, sandpipers, swans, and cranes.

For three miles the going was smooth, but then came a series of cascades. At length, there appeared three that were impassable. Linnaeus' guide turned in toward the shore, handed Linnaeus his possessions, then "laid his knapsack on his back, and turning the boat bottom upward, placed the oars longitudinally, so as to cross the seats. These rested on his arms as he carried the boat over his head, and thus he scampered away over the hills and valleys, so that the devil himself could not have come up with him."

At eight in the evening, Linnaeus and his scampering companion arrived at the home of the curate of Lycksele. The clergyman and his wife greeted Linnaeus hospitably and urged him to stay until the next fast day, in order that they could warn the Laplanders of his presence in the neighborhood. The Lapps were all too likely to fire a shot at strangers who came among them without some introduction.

The next morning, however, the clergyman realized that a thaw had set in and there was danger of bad flooding on the river. If Linnaeus delayed his journey, he might be caught in floodwater.

Linnaeus waited over until after church services the next day. In the meantime, he observed the Laplanders and their use of the reindeer, on which they depended

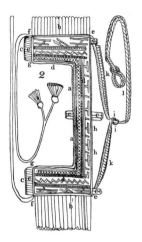

One of several drawings of the caparison of a reindeer, from Linnaeus' journal. This arrangement was worn over the reindeer's back. Linnaeus accompanied the drawing with a lengthy description of the device and its various parts.

for food, transportation, and clothing. He describes in his journal the whole caparison of a reindeer: bridle, saddle, harness, reins, even the stick used by the Lapps in driving this all-purpose animal.

On May 31 he left Lycksele with a guide, to travel toward Sorsele. He was now above the Arctic Circle. On June 1 he wrote: "We pursued our journey by water with considerable labor and difficulty all night long, if it might be called night, which was as light as the day, the sun disappearing for about half an hour only, and the temperature of the air being cold. The colonist who was my companion was obliged sometimes to wade along in the river, dragging the boat after him, for half a mile together. His feet and legs were protected by shoes made of birch bark."

In the morning the two men landed and went in search of a native Laplander who would be willing to guide Linnaeus on his journey. Three huts proved empty, so Linnaeus sent his companion to look farther on while he waited.

He described the dress of the Lapps in these parts: "On the head they wear a small cap, like those used at my native place of Stenbrohult, made with eight seams covered with strips of brown cloth, the cap itself being of a grayish color. This reaches no lower than the tips of the ears.

"Their outer garment, or jacket, is open in front halfway down the bosom, below which part it is fastened with hooks, as far as the pit of the stomach. Consequently the neck is bare, and from the effects of the sun abroad and the smoke at home, approaches the complexion of a toad. The jacket, when loose, reaches below the knees; but it is usually tied up with a girdle, so as scarcely to reach so far, and is sloped off at the bottom. The collar is of four fingers' breadth, thick, and stitched with thread.

"All the needlework is performed by the women. They make their thread of the sinews in the legs of the reindeer, separating them, while fresh, with their teeth, into slender strings, which they twist together. A kind of cord is also made of the roots of spruce fir."

When Linnaeus' companion returned, not having found another guide, the two proceeded up the river, whose waters were swollen by the melting snow. The wind blew very cold from the north.

Linnaeus goes on with his narrative: "At length, meeting with a very long, shelvy contraction in the river, we were obliged to quit our boat and go by land in search of a Laplander to serve as my guide farther on, whom we expected to find at a place a mile distant. But it appeared to me full a mile and a half, over hills and valleys, rivulets and stones. The hills were clad with ling and with *Empetrum*, which entangled our feet at every step; not to mention the trees lying in all directions in our way, and over which we were obliged to climb. The marshy spots were not less difficult to pass over. The bog moss afforded but a treacherous support for our feet, and the dwarf birch entangled our legs. . . .

"At length we came to a sort of bay, or creek, of the river, which we were under the necessity of wading through. The water reached our waists and was very cold. In the midst of this creek was so deep a hole that the longest pole could scarcely fathom it. We had no resource but to lay a pole across it, on which we passed over at the hazard of our lives; and indeed when I reached the other side, I congratulated myself on having had a very narrow escape. . . .

"We had next to pass a marshy tract, almost entirely under water, for the course of a mile, nor is it easy to conceive the difficulties of the undertaking. At every step we were knee-deep in water; and if we thought to

Linnaeus' drawing of a large kind
of gnat found in Lapland.

find a sure footing on some grassy tuft, it proved treacherous, and only sunk us lower. Sometimes we came
where no bottom was to be felt, and were obliged to
measure back our weary steps. Our half boots were filled
with the coldest water, as the frost, in some places, still
remained in the ground. . . . I wished I had never undertaken my journey, for all the elements seemed adverse.
It rained and blew hard upon us. . . .

"After having thus for a long time gone in pursuit of
my new Lapland guide, we reposed ourselves about six
o'clock in the morning, wrung the water out of our
clothes, and dried our weary limbs, while the cold north
wind parched us as much on one side as the fire scorched
us on the other, and the gnats kept inflicting their stings.
I had now my fill of traveling."

60

Finally a Laplander was found who went in search of a guide for Linnaeus. The young traveler wished to go back to Lycksele, the place from which he had started, but he dreaded returning by the same way he had come. He would gladly have taken a road, but there was none.

On June 3, at about two o'clock in the afternoon, the Laplander returned, worn out, but without a guide. Said Linnaeus: "He was accompanied by a person whose appearance was such that at first I did not know whether I beheld a man or a woman. . . . Her stature was very diminutive; her face of the darkest brown from the effects of smoke; her eyebrows black. Her pitchy-colored hair hung loose about her head, and on it she wore a flat red cap. She had a gray petticoat; and from her neck, which resembled the skin of a frog, were suspended a pair of large, loose breasts of the same brown complexion, but encompassed, by way of ornament, with brass rings. Around her waist she wore a girdle, and on her feet a pair of half boots."

At first, Linnaeus was frightened by her, but "though a Fury in appearance," she addressed him kindly, commiserating with him for having come to such a wretched spot.

He begged her to point out some direction he might go so that he would not have to return the way he had come. But she insisted that he must take the same route as before, since the river was in such bad flood that proceeding farther was impossible.

Linnaeus went on: "My health and strength being by this time materially impaired by wading through such an extent of marshes, laden with my apparel and luggage, for the Laplander had enough to do to carry the boat; by walking for whole nights together; by not having for a long time any boiled meat; by drinking a great quantity of water, as nothing else was to be had; and by eating nothing but fish, unsalted and crawling with vermin, I must have perished but for a piece of dried and salted reindeer's flesh, given me by my kind hostess the clergyman's wife at Lycksele."

He now inquired of the Lapp woman if she could give him anything to eat. She replied, "Nothing but fish." Linnaeus looked at the fresh fish she had, but saw that its mouth was full of maggots. He asked if he could have any reindeer tongues, for they were commonly dried for sale, but she had none. Finally, however, Linnaeus was able to buy from her a small cheese made of reindeer milk.

At long last, Linnaeus again arrived safely at the house of the curate in Lycksele and welcomed a meal of fresh meat. During the two days of rest that followed, he wrote many notes on the food, customs, dress, and hunting methods of the Lapps.

On June 8 he went back to Umeå. It was raining heavily, and his experiences beyond Lycksele had made him realize that it was still too early to go farther north. He spent the next few days in taking short expeditions around Umeå.

On June 12 he took his departure early, in hazy weather. Always the botanist, he wrote: "I wish those who deny that certain plants are peculiar to certain countries could see how abundantly the birch, the Lapland willow, the strawberry-leaved bramble, the cloudberry, and the thyme-leaved bellflower flourish in this district, and how the *Ranunculus acris* [buttercup] entirely covers the pasturelands with its brilliant yellow flowers."

He spent several days in the town of Piteå and then went on to Luleå, where he passed Midsummer Day in hunting for plants and minerals. By then the weather was warm and pleasant.

On June 25, after church, he left Luleå for Luleå Lappmark. Most of the day and night of June 27 he spent on a large sailing boat going up the Luleå River toward his destination.

Back on shore on June 29, he wrote miscellaneous observations about the Lapps: "The trees here produce *Usnea arborea* [a lichen] which the Laplanders apply to excoriations of the feet caused by excessive walking. They line their shoes with this moss, a practice which might with advantage be adopted by soldiers on a march. The Laplanders also line their shoes with grass, consisting of various species of *Carex*. This grass they comb with iron or horn combs, bruising it between their hands till it becomes soft and pliable. When dried, they cram it into their shoes, and it answers instead of stockings for defending the feet from the cold."

On July 1, Linnaeus for the first time saw the Lapland highlands, the Alps, in the distance. These were his goal. As he continued toward them he observed the Lapps, their customs, and their many ways of preparing reindeer milk for food. He made a variety of notes in his journal. Some of them make quaint reading today.

"The common method of the Laplanders for joining broken earthenware is to tie the fragments together with a thread, and boil the whole in fresh milk, by which they are cemented to each other. . . .

"An ointment for burns is made of fresh milk boiled to a thick consistency, with which the sore is anointed. It removes the pain, and admirably promotes the healing of the ulcer.

"For chilblains, the oil or fat which exudes from toasted reindeer cheese, rubbed upon the part affected, is a sovereign cure. Some persons use dog's fat for the same purpose. The latter is also used for pains in the back, being rubbed in before a fire."

On July 6 he found himself really in the Lapland Alps. "In the afternoon I took leave of Hyttan and in the distance of a mile from thence arrived at the mountain of Wallawari, a quarter of a mile in height. When I reached this mountain, I seemed entering on a new

Linnaeus' drawing of a flower
found in the Lapland Alps.

world; and when I had ascended it, I scarcely knew
whether I was in Asia or Africa, the soil, situation, and
every one of the plants being equally strange to me. Indeed I was now, for the first time, upon the Alps! Snowy
mountains encompassed me on every side. I walked in
snow as if it had been the severest winter. All the rare
plants that I had previously met with, and which had from
time to time afforded me so much pleasure, were here
as in miniature, and new ones in such profusion that I
was overcome with astonishment, thinking I had now
found more than I should know what to do with."

The alpine variety of the ptarmigans had hatched
their broods, and Linnaeus caught one of the chicks. The
hen, all concern, ran so close to him that he could easily
have caught her, too. As she continually jumped round

and round him he took pity on her and finally put the little chick back on the ground.

After having walked four or five miles more through the night, he went to sleep in the morning in one of the huts of the country. It had sixteen inhabitants, who were cordial but whose hygiene bothered Linnaeus a bit. "My hosts gave me *missen* to eat," he wrote. "That is whey, after the curd is separated from it, coagulated by boiling, which renders it very firm. Its flavor was good, but the washing of the spoon took away my appetite, as the master of the house wiped it dry with his fingers, whilst his wife cleaned the bowl, in which milk had been, in a similar manner, licking her finger after every stroke."

As Linnaeus climbed higher into the mountains he again noticed how dwarfed by the cold all the plants were. Birch trees crept mostly under the earth, throwing up the tips of their branches here and there to the height of only a few inches. Presently, as earlier near Lycksele, despair and fatigue overtook him. "We sought for one of the Laplanders' huts, but to no purpose. Tracks made by the reindeer were plentiful enough in the marshy grounds, which we followed sometimes in one direction, sometimes in another, without their leading us to what we were in search of. I had walked so much that I could hardly stand on my legs and was near fainting with fatigue, so that I lay down, resolving rather to endure the cold and boisterous wind than proceed farther this night."

The Lapland Journey

At length, his Lapp companions found what they were sure was the fresh track of a reindeer herd. They pursued it, and a half mile farther on found a Lapp camp. There Linnaeus was able to rest. He stayed in this spot for the following day and night, too tired to go on. During this time he took more notes on the Laplanders' way of living. He speaks in his journal of the great herds of reindeer that were driven home for milking morning and night. Even large numbers of the deer were easily controlled by a lone woman and a dog, and they readily obeyed a given word of command, especially if it was seconded by the hissing of the woman — a sound that apparently terrified them.

On July 11, Linnaeus and his guide arose early and continued on their way. They finally reached a high mountain where the streams flowed westward — a sign that the travelers had reached the divide and were now in Norwegian Lapland.

"The whole country was one dazzling, snowy waste," Linnaeus wrote. "The cold east wind quickened our steps and obliged us to protect our hands that we might escape chilblains. I was glad to put on an additional coat. As we proceeded across the north side of this mountain we were often so violently driven along by the force of the wind that we were taken off our feet and rolled a considerable way down the hill. This once happened to me in so dangerous a place that after rolling to the distance of a gunshot, I arrived near the brink of a precipice. . . . The rain, which fell in torrents on all sides, froze on our shoes and backs into a crust of ice. . . . At length, after having traveled betwixt three or four miles, the mountains appeared before us bare of snow, though only sterile rock, and between them we caught a view of the distant ocean. . . .

"Having thus traversed the Alps, we arrived about noon upon their bold and precipitous limits to the westward. The ample forests spread out beneath us looked like fine green fields. . . . We now descended into a lower country. . . . When we arrived at the plains below, how grateful was the transition from a chill and frozen mountain to a warm, balmy valley! I sat down to regale myself with strawberries. Instead of ice and snow I was surrounded by vegetation all in its prime. Such tall grass I had never before beheld in any country. Instead of the blustering wind so lately experienced, soft gales wafted around us the grateful scent of flowery clover and various other plants."

Linnaeus himself was exhausted, and he marveled to see how spry his two Lapp companions — one a man of fifty — remained. Now followed several days on the Norwegian seacoast. Linnaeus went fishing, and investigated the shore and its plants and animals, jellyfish among them.

On July 10 he arrived at the parsonage of John Rask, who had been to the West Indies and Africa and had published an account of his travels in which he described various fishes and plants. He received Linnaeus in a friendly manner, and the young man enjoyed his stay. "He has a handsome daughter, named Sarah Rask, eighteen years of age," observed Linnaeus. "She seemed to me uncommonly beautiful." Before he departed, the lovely Sarah gave to Linnaeus some recipes for making the Norwegian bread he had enjoyed during his stay.

On July 15, Linnaeus and his guides climbed up into the mountains again, on their return from the lowlands of Norway. "Our clothes, which were wet with perspiration in consequence of the heat we had encountered at the beginning of our journey, were now frozen stiff upon our backs by the cold," he wrote. "We determined to seek for a Laplander's hut. In order to get at one we were obliged to descend so steep a hill that, being unable to walk down it, I lay down on my back and slid along with the rapidity of an arrow from a bow."

Proceeding on their journey the next day, the travelers were caught in so thick a mist that, as Linnaeus wrote, their "situation was like that of an unskillful mariner at sea without a compass, out of sight of land and surrounded by hidden rocks on every side." Fortunately they stumbled upon the track of a reindeer and a sled, and following it, sought refuge in a Laplander's movable tent. In his journal, Linnaeus describes it in great detail and goes on to remark that all the Alps Laplanders were bleary-eyed because of the smoke in the tents, the fog, the sharp winds, and the severe cold.

All these Lapps of the high mountains lived in tents instead of huts. Within each tent were spread the skins of reindeer, hairy side up, on which the Lapps sat or lay down; the tents were not high enough for anyone to stand upright. In the center of each was a fireplace, and at the back was a brushwood screen, behind which was the household furniture: pots, kettles, bowls made of birch wood, and wooden boards that served as plates. Up in the roof of the tent two racks held cheeses laid to dry, and rennet bags filled with reindeer milk.

On July 17, Linnaeus saw lemmings, animals of this area, and remarked with pleasure that he found a little gentian flower. The next day he departed from the Alps, and since he now was in warmer country, tried to have some of his clothes washed. But the native people did not understand his request, as their clothing was made either of reindeer skins or of heavy wool, neither of which was washable.

The season was getting on, and the coming of the long arctic night was not far off. On July 24, Linnaeus remarked, "This night I beheld a star for the first time since I came within the Arctic Circle." Proceeding southward, he observed, "The purple willow herb made the fields at this time very beautiful. The goldenrod was also here in blossom."

He described the Lapps' sledges and skiis and also the reckoning of time. "The Laplanders use no almanac, but in its stead only a kind of instrument like the ancient runic calendar of the Goths, composed of seven small splinters or boards. . . . They do not, like us, compute time by the month, but by the course of their various holidays. They have also a name for every week. They are unable to tell when an eclipse of the sun or moon is to be expected. The year begins, by their reckoning, on the Friday before Christmas Day."

At sunset on July 26, Linnaeus reached Purkijaur. He and his guides tried in vain to hire a boat to go down-river. Finally they were obliged to make a raft. Because of a thick fog the night was dark, and they were swept into midstream, where their raft rapidly began to come apart. They managed to get to a house on an island, however.

Here Linnaeus hired a man to show him how fishing for freshwater pearls was conducted. The pearls were found in river mussels. He noted that the pearl in the mussel was not natural, but "a disease," and that if a person could cause the illness artificially he would be able to produce pearls as he wished. This idea stayed with Linnaeus and had its consequences much later in his life.

Going onward, the travelers were caught in a forest fire and later were terribly plagued by gnats. On July 30, Linnaeus was back in Luleå, where it rained and thundered violently all night long. A clean bed, good food, and the kind hospitality of his host, Pastor Un-naeus, more than made up for the inclement weather.

Rain continued all the next day, keeping Linnaeus from traveling to Torneå, in Finland.

On his way again, he observed on August 3, "At sunrise the marshes were all white with hoarfrost. In the preceding night, winter had paid his first visit."

At Torneå on August 4, Linnaeus knew his Lapland trip was at its end, and he thought of the things he had seen and the questions that had occurred to him. It might be worthwhile to find out if there were types of grain that would grow far north and might enrich the diet of the natives. And a comparative study of the Alps of Switzerland and Lapland might be rewarding. Greenland, too, should be studied, and its plants compared with those of Lapland. Ideas swarmed into his mind as he recalled his experiences.

At Torneå, also, Linnaeus sought to solve the mystery of a strange illness that seized the cattle each year. The natives were much puzzled by it. Linnaeus found it to be the result of the cattles' eating a plant, water hemlock. "A woman could eradicate all the plants in a month," he declared.

He took a homeward route down the coast of Finland. Still investigating, he observed the industries, the crops, and the plants. On September 3 he went to Biorknas to be instructed in assaying ores to find out their mineral content.

On September 14 he remarked, "The high wind scattered the withered leaves over my path. How useful are the usual storms of autumn to disperse ripe seeds and plant colonies far from the parent trees."

The autumn season was at its height. "The birch and the dwarf willows had now become pale, but the *Sorbus* [mountain ash] had assumed a red hue, as well as all the mosses. . . . I had frequent views of the sea through the woods on the right hand," he wrote on September 17.

Finally, on October 5, he took a ferry from Åbo, in Finland, to the island of Öland. Passing over Öland and taking another ferry, he arrived on the Swedish coast.

His entry on October 10 read, "About one o'clock in the afternoon I arrived at Uppsala.

"To the Maker and Preserver of all things be praise, honor, and glory forever!"

Linnaeus had traveled far and seen much. His journal is an amazing source of information about Lapland and the Lapps of his day. He had thought well in drawing up for the Scientific Society his list of a Lapland explorer's qualifications. Not only had he needed all the health, agility, and tirelessness he had recommended, but also he had needed and used all his knowledge and powers of observation. His account of the Lapps ranges widely and covers many subjects: household arrangements, cooking recipes, diseases and medicine, games and amusements, methods of fishing and catching seals, tanning reindeer leather, hop raising, betrothal and marriage ceremonies, bear-hunting methods, gluemaking from fish, clothing, plants, animals, and much, much else.

On May 12, 1732, Linnaeus had departed for Lapland as a youth on a lark. He returned in October as a seasoned traveler, more sure of himself and his abilities, more sharply observant, infinitely more sophisticated in his knowledge. Now he found himself an authority on Lapland — a young man with a recognized place in the world.

Back at Uppsala, he settled down to straightening out his accounts with the Scientific Society — a difficult task for him — and to making his report of the journey. In it he included a list of observations on plants, animals, and minerals and commented on the economic state of Lapland.

During the remainder of the university term he busied himself with writing *Flora Lapponica,* his manuscript on the plants of Lapland.

At Christmas he departed for Stenbrohult to visit his family, and arrived home on Christmas Eve, just as his father was saying grace.

TIME OF DECISION

UPON HIS RETURN TO UPPSALA, LINNAEUS
found himself in a bad situation. Once more,
poverty plagued him. He sadly missed the sal-
aries he had earned as the university's botanical
lecturer and the tutor of Rudbeck's children. To
make things worse, his royal scholarship was
about to expire. In order to secure at least a little
money, he applied to the Rector and Consistory
of the university, bluntly pointing out his grave

financial state and asking for help. Although the authorities reprimanded him for speaking so boldly and openly of such matters, they did give him some money to enable him to continue at Uppsala.

As for Linnaeus' studies, Rudbeck was still on his leave of absence, and now Roberg was serving for six months as Rector of the university and did even less lecturing than before. Rosén was still giving his anatomy lectures, but Linnaeus had already listened to these the previous year. And Rosén's botany lectures were certainly nothing that Linnaeus wanted to hear.

Under these circumstances he applied himself in 1733 to working at his own botanical research and his writing. *Flora Lapponica*, his guide to the plants of Lapland, and several other manuscripts were taking shape. In *Flora Lapponica*, Linnaeus had already given up the old Tournefort system of classifying plants by their flowers and fruits and was describing them according to their stamens and pistils. It is plain that his own system of plant classification was definitely crystallizing in his mind.

In addition to his research and writing, Linnaeus taught some private pupils in the natural sciences, and early in 1733 he began to give a private course of lectures in assaying ores. These lectures must have been based chiefly on the knowledge he had picked up during his Lapland tour.

The lectures proved popular, and Linnaeus even wrote

a short textbook on assaying. But Rosén objected to Linnaeus' setting himself up as a lecturer. There had been some unpleasantness between the two young men over the botany lectures. Each saw the other as a rival, and this situation made for unfriendliness between them. Moreover, Linnaeus was still a student and had no scholastic degree. Rosén and some of the other university teachers considered him an upstart. Linnaeus continued to give his private lectures throughout the summer term, however.

In December, 1733, he accepted an invitation to spend the Christmas holidays with Claes Sohlberg, a fellow student, at his home in the province of Dalarna. It was a jolly interlude for the serious young botanist. He met many of the young people of the district and joined in their dances and merrymaking.

But his searching mind never allowed him to relax for long. Dalarna was a mining region, and he could not resist the opportunity to learn about the minerals of the area. He visited a silver mine and a smelting plant, and he has left a vivid description of going deep into a copper mine by climbing down tier after tier of swaying wooden ladders and crawling on his hands and knees through shallow tunnels where the only light was a torch that he carried in his mouth. The darkness, the great depth, and the danger haunted him for a long time thereafter.

He did not return to Uppsala until early in 1734.

Once there, he unpacked his mineralogical specimens and began a new piece of writing, *Systema Lapideum (A Mineralogical System)*.

He had converted the room where he lived into a museum, decorating the ceiling with the feathers of birds, and one wall with a Lapp costume and other curiosities. In a corner of the high room he had put the branches of a tree, and here about thirty kinds of tame birds lived. On the window ledges grew rare plants in earthenware pots. In addition, he had his herbarium, now made up of over three thousand plant specimens from Sweden and Lapland. He also had a large collection of insects and minerals.

To his fellow students he seemed a fascinating fellow and they were interested in what he had to say. Once more he began private lectures in botany and also added a series of talks called "Natural Diet." His ideas on diet were advanced for his time; many of them are still sound. He recognized the value of fresh fruit and vegetables in the diet; advised moderation in eating; and warned against excessive use of alcohol — all these in the days when large quantities of meat were eaten and when overeating and overdrinking were both more common than today. His lecturing was popular, but it was still opposed by Rosén and some of the other university teachers and professors.

Linnaeus had come to a critical point in his life. He was twenty-seven years old and had spent seven years at

Lund and Uppsala. It was time to think of the future. More than anything else, he longed to be a teacher and professor at Uppsala. If that proved impossible, a doctor's career was his second choice. But a degree in medicine was necessary in order to hold either of these positions officially.

Legally it should have been possible to obtain a medical degree at either Lund or Uppsala. Actually the authorities at Uppsala recognized only a medical degree received abroad — and only a teacher with a foreign degree was accepted or promoted. At that time, Holland was famed for its medical schools, and in Holland the university at Harderwijk was the nearest, the least expensive, and the most popular for Swedish students. But going to Harderwijk took a fairly large sum of money — something Linnaeus did not have. His future looked problematical indeed. What should he do?

A definite answer to that question was postponed when he received a letter from Baron Reuterholm, the governor of the province of Dalarna. Linnaeus had met this gentleman during his Christmas visit with Claes Sohlberg. Now Governor Reuterholm enclosed some money and asked Linnaeus to undertake a trip through his province of Dalarna, reporting on it as he had on Lapland. Of course the young botanist was delighted. He quickly made himself ready and hastened to Falun, in Dalarna, to Reuterholm's house.

He had gained a good deal of prestige from his Lapland trip and since his return he had publicized his journey well. He loved to appear in the Lapp costume he had brought back from his travels, and so clothed, to talk about his adventures. They lost nothing in the telling, for Linnaeus had a vivid imagination and was never one to hide his light under a bushel. Now, when word of the upcoming Dalarna journey spread through the university, Linnaeus was besieged by students who wished to accompany him at their own expense.

In due time the Dalarna trip was organized as an expedition of young naturalists. Linnaeus selected seven of the best students from among the many volunteers. As head, or president, of the venture he drew up a list of laws and regulations and assigned certain duties to each of his assistants. Each member was to make a written report at the end of every day's journey.

A list of the duties reveals what traveling must have been like in those days, in a part of Sweden where hotels were a thing of the future and where no wheeled vehicles or public transportation were available.

These were the members of the expedition.

Reinhardt Näsman was the geographer. As a clergyman's son he also said morning and evening prayers and preached to the group on Sunday.

Carl Clewberg acted as naturalist on the four elements and on weather and the height of mountains. He also was secretary of the expedition.

Ingel Faldstedt was the mineralogist and, as groom,

saddled and attended to the horses that the group sometimes used for traveling.

Claes Sohlberg was the botanist and also the quarter-
master. He procured lodgings along the way and saw to
it that the group was provided with all necessities.

Eric Emporelius was the zoologist. He also shot game
and caught fish to help supply the company with food.

Peter Hedenblad acted as economist, reporting on the
clothing, houses, customs, and knowledge of medicine
of the native people. He also acted as adjutant to dis-
tribute Linnaeus' orders, and called the company together when necessary — especially in the evening, when
the account of the day's happenings was given. He saw
to it that the members of the group went to bed and got
up on time.

Bemain Sandel, an American from Pennsylvania, was
the steward and treasurer of the expedition. He took
care of obtaining fodder for the horses and buying wood
for the fire.

The arrangement worked well. The expedition was a
happy, friendly one. All the members were young, and
pleased to be away from the university for a while.
Faldstedt, athletic and good-natured, livened things up
when they became too solemn, while Näsman, a sober
young man, provided a little balance in the other direction. Claes Sohlberg led the way because Dalarna was
his home province and because it was his responsibility
to find quarters for the company at the end of the day

— sometimes in a barn or shack, sometimes in a dwelling house. The other members journeyed at a more leisurely pace, taking notes as they went along. Occasionally they divided into two groups that met at the end of the day. Since nearly one-quarter of the province was made up of lakes and rivers, they often traveled by boat.

The trip started on July 3, 1734, and ended forty-five days later. During its course, Linnaeus, as leader, learned much about directing the observations of his charges and winning their attention and respect. All this was to be useful to him later, in his career as a teacher.

The report of the journey covered the plant and animal life of the province as well as its minerals and other natural resources. In addition, a full account was given of the people's way of living: their dwellings; their habits of clothing, cooking, farming, hunting, and fishing; their diseases and medicinal remedies; their marriage customs, dances, and much else. This was a collection of valuable information, and it made Linnaeus realize how worthwhile a similar study of each of the provinces of Sweden would be. Each area was different and had many resources that at the time were not fully known.

The report pleased Governor Reuterholm. He was impressed with Linnaeus and asked the young student to stay on at Falun to tutor his sons in mineralogy and to teach assaying to them and to their regular tutor, Dr. Browallius. This was a happy circumstance for Linnaeus.

Life in the governor's home was pleasant. He was a comfortably wealthy man with a fine library that Linnaeus was free to use. There was ample spare time for the young botanist to go on with his own studies and writing. In fact, there was so much spare time that Linnaeus set up a medical practice of his own, and held public lectures on assaying ores.

He still had no medical degree, however, and he could not hope to have a long career either in medicine or in teaching without one. Dr. Browallius urged Linnaeus to go to Holland for his degree and advised him that, if all else failed, he should look for a wealthy young wife to furnish the necessary money.

Young Linnaeus became well known in Falun and was well liked. In November the father of Claes Sohlberg, his fellow student at Uppsala, offered to pay him a yearly fee if he would take Claes abroad and at the same time coach him in his studies. Here was the answer to Linnaeus' problem: the two students could go together to Holland. Linnaeus quickly accepted the offer and hurried back to Uppsala to take his theological examination. At that time any student wishing a passport to go abroad had first to show proof that he had passed such an examination.

Linnaeus arrived back at Falun on December 23, 1734, after a difficult journey on horseback through heavy snow. It was the holiday season and he joined happily in the festivities, going to dances and parties and having a thoroughly good time. At one of the parties he met Sara Elizabeth Moraea, eighteen years old, the daughter of Dr. Johann Moraeus, a wealthy physician of Falun. It was a case of strong mutual attraction. Soon Linnaeus, in his Lapland costume, was paying court to Sara Elizabeth. By January 16, the young people had agreed to consider themselves engaged.

This event was not altogether pleasing to Dr. Moraeus. He liked Linnaeus well enough, but Sara Elizabeth had grown up in a wealthy and socially important family — her father had hoped for a better match for her. Linnaeus was poor and a botanist — a young man without prospects, in Dr. Moraeus' view. Finally, however, on February 18, 1735, an agreement was reached. Dr. Moraeus consented to permit an informal engagement, but decreed that no formal betrothal was to take place for three years. In the meantime, Linnaeus was to go abroad as he had planned, and get his degree. Dr. Browallius, the tutor of Governor Reuterholm's sons, agreed to forward Sara Elizabeth's letters to Linnaeus, wherever he might be. What Dr. Moraeus' secret thoughts on the engagement were, no one knows. After all, three years is a long time, and perhaps —

On February 20, 1735, Linnaeus and his fellow traveler Claes Sohlberg set out from Falun. The snowy, wintry weather was atrocious and the two companions journeyed slowly, stopping to visit friends along the way.

They did not reach Växjö, in southern Sweden, until March 12. Here they visited Linnaeus' old friend Dr. Rothman before they went on to Stenbrohult, where they arrived on March 19.

Linnaeus' mother had died some time earlier and he missed her badly. But on the whole the visit was a contented one. The travelers stayed for nearly a month. At last, just as the birch trees were beginning to open their leaves and the rye to spring green through the soil, the two young men took to the road again.

On April 19, 1735, they set out from Helsingborg, Sweden, for Elsinore, Denmark, on the first lap of their journey to Holland.

HOLLAND INTERLUDE

LINNAEUS AND SOHLBERG SPENT FOUR DAYS
in Elsinore, hoping to find a sailing ship that
would take them directly to Holland. But none
was available and at last they went aboard a vessel bound for Lübeck, Germany. Several more
days passed before the ship finally raised anchor
and got under way. In the meantime it lay in the
sound outside Elsinore alongside a multitude of
other vessels, all waiting for the wind to change

to a favorable quarter. Since the sea was rough and rolling, shipboard life was far from pleasant and many of
the passengers on board were seasick. Linnaeus and his
friend endured discomfort and the disagreeable smell
of bilge water, however, rather than spend more money
for a room at an inn on shore.

At last a good wind arose; the sails were quickly
raised, the anchor was hauled up, and the vessel was on
its way. Two days later, Linnaeus and Sohlberg arrived
at Travemunde, in Germany. From there they went by
stagecoach to Lübeck. Linneaus, a landlubber of the
first order, gloried in being back among the fields and
woods and took careful note of the growing plants he
saw along the way.

From Lübeck the travelers continued to Hamburg by
post diligence — a mail coach drawn by six horses, three
abreast. Although the interior of the coach was reserved
for mail and baggage, there was room for six passengers
to sit outside. The forty-eight-mile trip took twelve
hours. "The nightingale sang all the way," noted Linnaeus in his account of the journey.

Hamburg was a delightful surprise to the two young
men. They enjoyed the fine gardens, the museums, the
attractive houses, and the cordiality of the inhabitants.
Here, for the first time, Linnaeus found himself something of an international celebrity. In a bookshop he
found copies of a German newspaper in which there
were favorable accounts of his Lapland trip. At the

same time, Johann Kohl, Professor of Humanities at the Hamburg Gymnasium and editor of a Hamburg periodical, had published pieces praising Linnaeus' *Hortus Uplandica* and some of the papers he had written.

When Professor Kohl heard that Linnaeus was in Hamburg he quickly made himself known to the young botanist. Kohl was a hospitable man and introduced Linnaeus to various of his scientific friends. Soon these men were inviting the young Swede to their homes, lending him books, and showing him their collections of rare plants and fossils. Linnaeus was thoroughly pleased to know these scientists and to have an opportunity to read several of the botanical books he had long heard of but had never seen. "It was like coming into a large inheritance of unknown treasures," he later wrote.

For his part, Linnaeus too had much to offer. He had brought with him his manuscripts so that they might be published in Holland, long a European center for printing. He had his Lapp costume and was not backward about showing it and describing his adventures in Lapland. He had his insect collection, which was an impressive sight. He was young and attractive and enthusiastic, and his Hamburg friends found him stimulating company.

In the end, his enthusiasm for learning and his tendency to show off his knowledge were almost his undoing in Hamburg. One of the wonders of the city was a stuffed, seven-headed, so-called hydra that belonged in the natural history collection of the burgomaster. It had originally been brought as loot from Prague at the end of the Thirty Years' War. Of course, Linnaeus was taken to view this remarkable object. Always sharp-eyed, he quickly saw that it was a fraud. Its dragon-like body was made of snake skins glued together. To this body seven weasel heads had been attached.

Linnaeus was too impulsive and too talkative to keep his discovery to himself. But, as it happened, this was a singularly bad time to make known his findings, for the burgomaster was dickering with a prospective buyer of this great natural history curiosity. When news of the hydra's true nature spread, the price was bound to go plummeting downward and the burgomaster was bound to be exceedingly angry. Linnaeus' Hamburg friends quietly advised him that perhaps the time had come for him to continue his journey. He left Hamburg on May 16, 1735.

The next day, he and Sohlberg boarded a ship headed for Amsterdam, in Holland. First, contrary winds, and then no winds at all, delayed them, but they finally arrived in Amsterdam on June 2. After spending several days in exploring the city, they sailed again — this time for Harderwijk, a little town on the southeastern shore of the Zuider Zee.

The day after his arrival at Harderwijk, Linnaeus enrolled at the university and handed in his thesis, which he had already written before he left Sweden. This thesis set forth a new theory on the cause of intermittent fever. At that time, Linnaeus believed it came only to those people who lived where the soil was composed of clay; later on, he changed his mind about this.

On the same day, he was required to take an oral medical examination, and write an essay on some of the ideas of Hippocrates, the ancient Greek physician. In addition, he was requested to give an oral argument on what he had written. He was then asked to diagnose a case of jaundice and prescribe for it. After this, he was declared a Medical Candidate.

The next day, his thesis was given back to him and he rushed it to the printer. Once it had been printed, he was to defend its contents in a public debate. But while he waited he spent the time in attending lectures and in sightseeing.

At last the day of the debate came and he defended his thesis successfully. Now he was presented with his diploma, a doctor's gold ring, and a silk hat; his name was written in the register of doctors. The long-awaited time had come: he had received his medical degree and was a full-fledged doctor of medicine.

He wished for nothing better at this point than to start for home, but his old trouble, lack of money, nagged at him again. The fee from the father of Sohlberg had not been paid, and Linnaeus later wrote that "now all the money he [Linnaeus] had carried with him from Sweden was expended, and being unwilling to trouble his future father-in-law, whose disposition he well knew on this score, he accompanied Claes Sohlberg from Harderwijk to Amsterdam." Apparently Sohlberg paid the living expenses. The two young men made the journey on foot.

In Amsterdam, Linnaeus set about making the acquaintance of the community's scientific men. From Amsterdam the travelers went on to Leiden. There they visited the botanical garden and Adrian van Royen, a professor of botany. One of the most valuable friends Linnaeus made in Leiden, however, was Dr. Johann Friedrich Gronovius, a physician. After Linnaeus had called on Dr. Gronovius, the doctor returned the visit. In Linnaeus' lodgings Gronovius saw the manuscript of the young botanist's *Systema Naturae* (*A System of Nature*), a scheme for grouping and classifying the animal, plant, and mineral kingdoms of the world. Gronovius was so deeply impressed with it that he asked Linnaeus' permission to have it printed at his own expense.

Since that would take time, Linnaeus was invited to stay with his new friend, Dr. Gronovius, in the interim. Gronovius introduced him to many of the scholars of Leiden, which was still an important university town. Among the men whom Linnaeus met was Isaac Lawson, a learned and wealthy Scotsman who was Physician General to the army of Flanders. Lawson joined with Gronovius in paying the expenses of printing *Systema Naturae*.

Portrait of Carl Linnaeus as a young man. Painting by J. H. Scheffel, and now at Hammarby, Sweden. Linnaeus wears a scarlet coat with gold buttons.

This work was finally published in 1735. Although it was later republished and enlarged many times, this first printed edition was only twelve pages in length. (Each page, it is true, was almost the size of a modern newspaper page.) Short though the book was, it was of tremendous importance. It set forth Linnaeus' view of the natural history kingdoms and contained the first inkling of the scheme for classifying the things of nature that was afterward adopted over many parts of the world.

In Leiden, Linnaeus found another staunch friend in Dr. Hermann Boerhaave. At that time, Boerhaave was considered Europe's most eminent physician and was famous for his knowledge of botany and chemistry as well. From all directions, visitors flocked to see Boerhaave. It was exceedingly difficult to gain an audience with him. Linnaeus had come to Leiden partly in the hope of meeting this famous man, but that seemed an impossibility. Gronovius, however, suggested that Linnaeus write a letter to Boerhaave. To his surprise, the young Swede received an answer granting him an interview a week later — record time for making an appointment with the busy doctor.

Apparently Boerhaave, then sixty-seven years old, was charmed with the younger man. He made an appointment to see Linnaeus again, only a few days after the first meeting, at his country home outside Leiden. Here Boerhaave had a large and elaborate garden in which was planted every kind of tree that could endure the climate. For recreation and relaxation he loved to work in this garden.

Although he was one of the richest men in Leiden, Boerhaave was plain and unassuming. He usually owned only two suits at a time; these he wore until they were threadbare. With his solidly built figure, old shoes, slightly unkempt hair, and the large stick he often carried, he looked like anything but the wealthy scholar he was. But although parsimonious with himself, he was generous in his help to others.

Now, as he and Linnaeus walked about Boerhaave's garden, the old doctor was surprised at Linnaeus' scientific knowledge of the exotic plants that grew there. One tree Boerhaave pointed out as a great rarity that had never been described by any botanist. Linnaeus was quick to differ. It was the white hornbeam, he declared; it grew in many parts of Sweden. Moreover, he asserted, Vaillant had described it in his work *A Parisian Botany*. Boerhaave was sure that Linnaeus must be wrong, as Boerhaave himself had been in charge of the publication of this book. Linnaeus was courteous, but he held to his opinion. Vaillant's book was sent for and Linnaeus found the description in it. He had been right. More than ever, Boerhaave was pleased with the Swedish botanist's knowledge.

The days rolled by, and at last Linnaeus went to make a final visit to Boerhaave before returning to Sweden — or so he thought. Boerhaave urged him not to leave

Holland, but to settle there and make a career of botany. He suggested that, in any case, Linnaeus stop in Amsterdam and pay a call on Johannes Burman, a professor of botany and the superintendent of the Amsterdam Botanical Garden.

Burman was a man of Linnaeus' own age, whom Linnaeus had previously met. Now, with Boerhaave's sponsorship, the Swedish botanist found Burman much more cordial than formerly. Burman showed Linnaeus his herbarium and pointed out a plant that he considered almost unknown in Europe. Linnaeus asked for a single flower and, thinking of his system for identifying plants, declared the flower to be that of a *Laurus*. Burman disagreed, but Linnaeus was firm, saying, moreover, that the blossom was that of the cinnamon tree. Now Burman was surprised, for Linnaeus had identified the flower correctly. The Swedish botanist then explained why, according to his views, the *Laurus* and the cinnamon should be united into one group. He went on to correct some of Burman's other plant classifications.

At this time, Burman was preparing a great work on the plants of Ceylon. Impressed with Linnaeus' botanical knowledge, he offered the Swedish visitor a handsome set of rooms in his house and board at his table if he would stay and help with the book. Linnaeus readily agreed to this suggestion. At about the same time, Claes Sohlberg paid Linnaeus some of the money due him. Once again, the world looked hopeful to Linnaeus.

During his stay, Linnaeus found time to study in Burman's library and to complete some of his own writings for publication. One of the works he finished and had printed was *Fundamenta Botanica* (*Botanical Foundations*), a small volume that set forth in brief aphorisms Linnaeus' theory of botany and presented the fundamental rules to be observed in the classification and naming of plants. It showed the basis for Linnaeus' new system of grouping plants.

But now, once again, Dr. Boerhaave stepped in to change the course of Linnaeus' life. One of Boerhaave's patients was George Clifford, an extremely rich banker who was also one of the directors of the Dutch East India Company. Like many wealthy Europeans of that time, Clifford made a hobby of gardening and botany. Because of his connection with the Dutch East India Company, which sent ships to far-off places in the Orient, he was able to collect many rare plants and animals. His estate, Hartecamp, near Haarlem, was famous for its greenhouses, its menagerie, its exotic garden, and its very great luxury.

Clifford had not been well, and he went to Dr. Boerhaave for advice. The doctor suggested that it would be beneficial for his patient to have a personal physician on his estate to supervise his treatment and diet and to report back to Boerhaave. Moreover, said Boerhaave, he knew just the man for the position. He spoke of Linnaeus and, after recommending him highly as a doctor, added, "And he can look after your garden, too."

Clifford was interested, sought out Linnaeus at Burman's, and invited the two gentlemen to Hartecamp to see his greenhouses and plants. The visit went well. Clifford was pleased with the young doctor-botanist. Soon after, he suggested that Linnaeus take the position on his estate.

Much as Linnaeus would have liked to accept Clifford's offer, he hesitated to leave Burman, to whom he owed loyalty. The story is told that on a visit with Linnaeus to Clifford's home, Burman chanced to see lying on a table the second volume of a book by Sir Hans Sloane. It was a book that Burman longed to own, and he was examining it with great interest when Clifford remarked that he had two copies and would give Burman one if, in return, Burman would release Linnaeus to come to Hartecamp. The offer of exchanging Linnaeus for a book was jokingly made, but soon, in dead earnest, Clifford completed a salary arrangement with Linnaeus.

"Thus," wrote Linnaeus, who almost always referred to himself in the third person, "Linnaeus moved to Clifford's where he lived like a prince; had one of the finest gardens in the world under his inspection, with commission to procure all the plants that were wanting in the garden, and such books as were not to be found in the library; and of course enjoyed all the advantages he could wish for in his botanical labors, to which he devoted himself day and night."

THE HARTECAMP YEARS

WITH HIS CHEERFUL AND CHARMING WAYS,
Linnaeus was quickly accepted by the members
of Clifford's household and came to feel greatly
at home there. Since he had never known wealth,
life at Hartecamp was a continual wonder to him.
In later times he often described the two years
he spent with Clifford as the most pleasant he
had ever experienced. Besides the luxurious
house itself, there were the greenhouses and gar-

dens with their treasure of plants, and there was the happy freedom from financial worry — all entrancing to him.

In spite of his travels, Linnaeus never learned to speak any languages but Swedish and Latin and never attempted to; his mind was concentrated on other things that seemed more important to him. He had no trouble in communicating with the learned men of his day, since Latin was still widely used among scholars, but his inability to speak the language of Holland did prevent his becoming acquainted with the Dutch young people. At Hartecamp, instead of leading a social life natural to a young man in his twenties, he devoted himself almost entirely to work. Clifford had a large herbarium which Linnaeus busied himself with arranging. Each month he visited the botanical gardens at Amsterdam, Utrecht, and Leiden, where he obtained new plant specimens which he dried and added to Clifford's collection. A daily acquaintance with Hartecamp's gardens also added greatly to Linnaeus' botanical knowledge.

At Hartecamp he occupied himself with his own writings too. Some of them he had already roughed out at Uppsala. But now, with his increased knowledge and with the opportunity to use Clifford's library, Linnaeus found that the work he had previously started needed revision. He labored hard at this, driven by an urgent need to express the thoughts that crowded his mind.

During this time an unexpected pleasure came to him.

One day, on the streets of Leiden, he came face-to-face with his old friend Peter Artedi, whom he had not seen since before his Lapland journey. Artedi, just arrived from England, was despondent. His British stay had been cut short by lack of money; he had no extra clothes; he wished only to get his medical degree and return home. But without funds there seemed to be no way to do this.

Here Linnaeus was delighted to assist. In Amsterdam was an apothecary, Albert Seba, who was writing a book, *A Treasury of Natural History.* A short time before Artedi arrived, Seba had asked Linnaeus to help him with the third volume, but Linnaeus had already begun his work with Clifford. As it happened, Seba's third volume was about fishes, which were Artedi's specialty. Linnaeus journeyed to Amsterdam with his friend, and Seba gladly hired Artedi to help him.

Happy to know that his friend was provided for, Linnaeus once more plunged into his work at Hartecamp. He arranged to see Artedi whenever he could, but for the most part his head was full of his own plans. Linnaeus visited Artedi on September 25, 1736, and found him still gloomy. Artedi, usually so quiet, was obviously pleased to see Linnaeus and unburdened himself to him. He drew out all the manuscripts he had written, showed them to Linnaeus, and told of his intention of finishing them, once the work with Seba was done. When Linnaeus rose to go, Artedi was oddly reluctant to part from him. Later, looking back, Linnaeus wondered that he had felt no foreboding, and deeply regretted that he had not stayed with Artedi longer, for he never again saw his friend alive. A short time after Linnaeus' visit, Artedi went to dine with Seba. Returning home late at night, he stumbled in the darkness into one of Amsterdam's canals and was drowned. His body was found the next day.

Linnaeus did not hear of Artedi's death until three days after it occurred. Shocked at the news, he rushed to Amsterdam and to the apothecary Seba, who gave him a small sum of money for Artedi's funeral expenses. It was an occasion of deep sorrow to Linnaeus when he viewed the lifeless body of his friend. He thought of Artedi's talent and bright hopes and the start he had made in his writing. In that hour of mourning, Linnaeus determined to honor the promise he had made years before at Uppsala — to see that Artedi's work was published for all the world to know.

Artedi's manuscripts were at his lodging house, and the landlord, realizing their value, refused to give them up until the rent owed him by Artedi was paid. When Clifford came forward with the money, Linnaeus gained permission from Artedi's relatives to edit his friend's work and have it published. He gave his time generously to the task. Artedi's *Ichthyologia* (*A Discourse on Fishes*) appeared two years later, in 1738, with a preface by Linnaeus.

In the meantime, Linnaeus was becoming restless. He wished to take a trip to England to see the British botanists and their gardens and to bring back new plant specimens for his patron. Clifford arranged that the journey should be taken at his expense, but asked that Linnaeus be gone only eight days. In view of the uncertain traveling conditions of the period, this was an impossible time limit. As usual, Linnaeus met with an unfavorable wind upon sailing, and it took him a week to reach England from Rotterdam.

In London he stayed with the pastor of the Swedish Church. As he did not speak English or understand it, there was danger of his losing his way while traveling about the city. An envelope with the pastor's address written on it is still in existence in the library of the Linnean Society in London. This, it is said, was carried about by Linnaeus during his London visit, to be shown in case he lost his bearings and needed direction.

In spite of his language difficulties, Linnaeus saw a good deal of the city. He went to the theater, and one Sunday he attended the Foundling Chapel where he heard George Frederick Handel conduct some of his own music. In addition, he visited various botanists in the area and obtained plants for Clifford.

From London, Linnaeus traveled to Oxford to see the university's gardens and its famous botanist, Johann Dillenius. To Linnaeus' surprise, Dillenius greeted him with coldness and dislike. Linnaeus was at a loss to understand why, until Dillenius, knowing that Linnaeus did not understand English, spoke in his presence to a fellow botanist, an Englishman. "Here is the young man who would confound all botany," he said. Because the words "confound" and "botany" have their roots in classical Latin and Greek, Linnaeus had a general idea of the nature of Dillenius' remark.

When Dillenius continued to be discourteous to him, Linnaeus resolved to leave Oxford the next day, but he was determined, before he went, to find out why Dillenius had spoken of him in so disparaging a way. Upon being questioned, Dillenius refused to discuss the remark. When Linnaeus persisted, however, Dillenius pulled out the proof sheets of the first half of Linnaeus' own book, *Genera Plantarum* (*The Genera of Plants*), which was then being printed in Leiden. In it Linnaeus had reclassified many plants according to his own system. Gronovius, thinking that the proof sheets would interest Dillenius, had sent them to him. The English botanist had gone over them and had found that Linnaeus differed from many of Dillenius' classifications. On almost every page there were notes in Dillenius' handwriting, marking Linnaeus' classifications as false.

Linnaeus held fast to his views, however, and he and Dillenius went into the garden and examined some of the flowers in question. When Dillenius found that Linnaeus was actually right, all his former coldness disappeared. He begged Linnaeus to stay longer at Oxford and promised him plants for Clifford's garden.

Linnaeus remained in Oxford for several more days, during which he explored the countryside, took trips with Dillenius, met Dillenius' friends, and became acquainted with the university's Bodleian and Botanical libraries. In these libraries he found Thomas Millington's writings on the sex of plants, published in 1670, even before Vaillant's.

When Linnaeus finally left Oxford, Dillenius parted from him reluctantly. Dillenius still had doubts about Linnaeus' system of plant classification, however. Soon after Linnaeus' departure the English botanist wrote a friend that the young Swede had a thorough knowledge of botany, but he added, "I am afraid his method will not hold."

Although Linnaeus greatly enjoyed his visit to England, he felt he must not stay long. He had collected many dried plants for Clifford's herbarium as well as live plants for the garden at Hartecamp. There was much work to be done in tending these new treasures and studying them. Back at Hartecamp, he was caught up again in his strenuous routine.

In 1737, his book *Genera Plantarum*, whose proofs Dillenius had received at the time of Linnaeus' English visit, was finally published. In this same year, Linnaeus labored hard over *Hortus Cliffortianus (Clifford's Garden)*, an enormous work he was writing for Clifford, describing the plants in Hartecamp's greenhouses and garden. Such rarities as the tea, coffee, and cacao plants were described, and the book was illustrated with beautiful colored engravings. When it was finished, *Hortus Cliffortianus* numbered 501 large pages. Linnaeus had written and arranged the manuscript, then corrected the printed proofs, all in nine months. It was a mammoth task, but he still found time to work occasionally at another of his botanical writings, *Critica Botanica*, which was an enlargement of some of the rules first set forth in *Fundamenta Botanica*.

Now he had become well known among a circle of scientific friends in Holland. As recreation from the work of composing *Hortus Cliffortianus* he went occasionally to Amsterdam to visit Burman, or dropped in at Boerhaave's lectures in Leiden. Van Royen and Lawson showed him every hospitality and he was always an especially welcome guest in Gronovius' household. Wherever he went, his old standby, the Lapp costume, proved a huge success. Boerhaave's friends, particularly, took delight in seeing Linnaeus wear it as he told of his adventures in Lapland.

By the fall of 1737, *Hortus Cliffortianus* was finished. Worn out from his work, and homesick besides, Linnaeus wished to start for Sweden. Clifford was saddened to see him go and tried in every way to change his intention, but Linnaeus could not be persuaded. Saying goodbye to his benefactor, he set out for Leiden. As a parting gift and a sign of his appreciation of the superb work done on *Hortus Cliffortianus*, Clifford gave the younger man a sizable sum of money.

In Leiden, Linnaeus' many friends were dismayed at the thought of his leaving. Professor van Royen was particularly upset. He had recently received a grant of money to use in putting the university gardens in order, and he wished Linnaeus' help with the project. He proposed that the plants in the garden should all be labeled anew with names given them according to Linnaeus' system of plant classification.

This suggestion attracted Linnaeus, but it also placed him in a difficult situation. His good friend Dr. Boerhaave had originally arranged and named the plants according to a system of his own. True, other botanists ignored this system, but Linnaeus still feared he might offend Boerhaave if he changed it. He finally reached a compromise, agreeing to spend the next few months with van Royen, working out a special system — not entirely the Linnaean one — with some new names. Van Royen further requested that Linnaeus should demonstrate his foundations of botany to the university students and set up a future course of study for them.

When Clifford heard of Linnaeus' new employment he was indignant, as he felt that he had a prior claim to the botanist's services. Linnaeus finally smoothed the matter over by persuading Clifford that any work he did for van Royen would reflect credit on Clifford and his gardens. So the affair was settled.

In Leiden, Linnaeus lived well at van Royen's expense. His work was not as grueling as it had been for the past two years, and he felt fairly carefree and prosperous. He now had an opportunity to see his many Leiden friends more frequently. They made him a member of a club that Lawson, Gronovius, Boerhaave, and some of the other local men of science had formed. At the weekly Saturday meetings the host for the occasion took charge and discussed something in his own field of interest. Lawson discussed ancient history; Gronovius, botany; Linnaeus, natural history. Using Linnaeus' classification tables, the club members learned to identify plants, fishes, and minerals — even those they had never seen before. At first there had been some doubt about the worth of Linnaeus' system, but soon the men were looking forward to his demonstrations as eagerly as they might to a game of skill.

During his Leiden stay, Linnaeus found time also to help Gronovius with some of his botanical writing, and himself published *Classes Plantarum* (*The Classes of Plants*), and some other volumes.

In the spring, however, bad news came. A Swedish friend of Linnaeus' wrote to sound the alarm. Browallius, the tutor to Reuterholm's sons — and the man who had been posting Sara Elizabeth's letters to Linnaeus — had been appointed a university professor at Åbo. He was courting Sara Elizabeth in dead earnest, seeking to convince her that Linnaeus would never return, and trying to persuade her to marry himself instead.

Horrified at this threat to his plans, Linnaeus decided to leave for Sweden as soon as possible. Although he was tired and run down, had a fever, and felt far from well, he hurriedly made his arrangements to depart. His friend Isaac Lawson gave him a generous farewell party at which oysters, a favorite treat, were served. The next day, Linnaeus was seriously ill with what he afterward called cholera. Now Clifford stepped in and persuaded him to come back to Hartecamp to stay until he had fully recovered. It was over six weeks before Linnaeus was again able to travel.

Before he left Holland he paid a last call on Boerhaave, who was now a very sick man and knew that he did not have long to live. He was no longer able to see visitors, but Linnaeus was allowed to enter the sickroom. There he raised the hand of the weak old man and kissed it in respectful salute. With great effort, Boerhaave lifted Linnaeus' hand to his lips. "What the world has required from me, it has got, but the world requires still much more from thee. Good-bye, my dear Linnaeus," he said. Tears blinded Linnaeus' eyes as he walked from the room. At his lodgings he received a handsome copy of Boerhaave's *Chemistry*, a final gift from the old doctor. Boerhaave died soon afterward.

At last the day of Linnaeus' departure from Hartecamp came, although Clifford urged him to stay. Lin-

naeus packed a trunk with the writings he had finished
during his almost three years in Holland — fourteen
published books and many short treatises. It was as important a collection of botanical works as had ever been
written by one man, and was to change the science of
botany forever after.

Clifford accompanied his friend in his own carriage
to the Hague, and from there to Delft. For, in spite of
Linnaeus' seeming anxiety about Sara Elizabeth, he was
not going directly home, but to Paris instead.

Upon his arrival in that city he was invited to be the
guest of Antoine de Jussieu, a famous professor of medicine and a lecturer on botany at the Royal Garden of
Paris. Jussieu had a younger brother, Bernard, who was
also a professor of botany. It was Bernard who took
Linnaeus under his protection, showed him the sights of
the city and the things of botanical and scientific interest, and introduced him to many of the French scientists.

Among other hospitalities, Linnaeus was invited to
attend a meeting of the French Academy of Sciences.
There he had a most encouraging surprise: the members
of the Academy were anxious that he become a Foreign
Correspondent of the society, but they offered, if he
would become a French citizen, to appoint him a full
member with an annual pension. The offer was flattering
and well worth considering seriously, but Linnaeus was
still determined to return to Sweden, and so refused the
full membership.

In all, he spent a month in Paris — a stimulating month during which he was cordially received as a recognized and important scientist and mingled on equal terms with the great men of science whom he met. At the end of this time he was becoming short of money, however, and decided to take the most inexpensive way home. He sailed from Rouen — with a favorable wind, for once — and went directly to Sweden.

Upon his arrival he immediately headed for his childhood home, Stenbrohult, there to spend a few days with his father and to put before him the tangible results of his Holland years — the books and treatises he had written. Then he went on to Falun and Sara Elizabeth, who was still waiting patiently for him.

At Falun the reunion was a happy one, and Linnaeus and his future wife were at last formally betrothed. But Sara Elizabeth's father continued to be cautious. There were as yet no openings for a teacher at Uppsala, and botany by itself still seemed an unprofitable occupation to Dr. Moraeus. He insisted that his future son-in-law must have a good means of livelihood before a marriage could take place.

Once again, Linnaeus set out, this time to seek a living as a medical doctor in Stockholm, Sweden. And once again, Sara Elizabeth resigned herself to waiting.

THE SUM OF THE WORK

IN 1738, WHEN HE WENT TO STOCKHOLM,
Linnaeus was thirty-one — still a young man —
yet already much of his most valuable work had
been done. During the time he had spent in Holland he had published fourteen books on botany.
Many of them were of the utmost importance to
the future of that science. Though some of this
work had first been written during his student
years at Uppsala, Linnaeus had found new op-

portunities for study in Holland's libraries and had thoroughly revised his earlier manuscripts, in addition to writing some entirely new ones.

Botany is a subject that requires meticulous, time-consuming research, and Linnaeus' own ideas had demanded many hours of careful thought besides. The wonder is that one man could have turned out such a tremendous amount of significant writing in so short a time.

Only a person like Carl Linnaeus could have done so much. He was possessed of tremendous energy and drive, a passion for work, an overpowering enthusiasm for botany, and an urgent sense that he had something vital to contribute to that science. Helpful too was his situation in Holland. At Hartecamp he had been free from financial worry and the small mechanics of daily living that eat up so much of the time for many persons. The best of libraries had been literally at his elbow, and he had profited by Clifford's approval and encouragement.

Outside Hartecamp had been a ring of influential and sympathetic friends who were prepared to assist him in every possible way. Lawson, Boerhaave, Gronovius, and others had stood always ready to advise him or to assume the tasks that would have kept him from his writing.

Gronovius appears in the front ranks of those who made Carl Linnaeus' books possible. Since Linnaeus did not speak Dutch, it was Gronovius who dealt with the printers and saw the books through the press. More than

that, he went over Linnaeus' manuscripts before publication, smoothing out the Latin, correcting inconsist-
encies, and offering constructive criticism. Later he read
the proofs. A man of infinite generosity and patience,
Gronovius expended endless time on Linnaeus' books.
It is said that he once spent six days on the correction of
a single plate for Linnaeus' *Flora Lapponica.*

In order to understand just what Linnaeus accomplished during his Holland years, it is necessary to know
how plants are classified today, and why.

There are now over 300,000 kinds of plants known
in the world. Some method must be used to identify
them readily. This is done by classification. Classification means putting into a series of groups those plants
that have similar basic characteristics and seem to have
some relationship to each other, naming them and briefly
describing the identifying marks of each group and each
kind of plant.

To identify a plant, a description that fits it and no
other kind must be found among the many, many groups.
It would be almost impossible to pinpoint a plant correctly at once, so identification is usually done by easy
stages. First, the seeker finds a large group of plants
whose description lists some general characteristics in
common with the plant he is identifying. Within that
large group he then finds a smaller group with a slightly
more particular description that fits his plant. In the
smaller group he again narrows his choice, and so on,

until at last he arrives at a description listing character-istics that apply absolutely to his plant and no other kind.

There is an orderly system of arrangement. The basic unit of grouping is the *species*. (This is what an identifier seeks to find.) A species is one definite *kind* of plant. Its members have similar structure and characteristics, breed with one another, and ordinarily reproduce to be much alike from generation to generation. For instance, the white clover is a species. Its scientific name is *Trifolium repens*.

There are other kinds of clovers, however. All of them have a certain type of leaf and flower and fruit. All the clovers are obviously related one to another, al-though not as closely as the white clovers are to each other. Each kind of clover plant is a species. All the species of clover plants go together into a *genus*. A genus is a group of closely related species. To show their close relationship, all the species of a genus have the same first name. So, all the clovers are called *Trifolium* (meaning "three-leaved"). But whereas the white clover is called *Trifolium repens*, the red clover is called *Tri-folium pratense*. *Trifolium* is the genus, or generic, name; the second name is the species, or specific, name. The scientific name of a plant is made up of its generic and specific names combined.

The grouping that is next larger than the genus is the *family*. Clovers have some characteristics, such as similar flowers and fruits, in common with alfalfas, lupines, peas, and many other plants. Peas have the generic name *Pisum*; alfalfas have the generic name *Medicago*; lupines have the generic name *Lupinus*. But all these plants and many others, including the clovers, are grouped in the same family and have the same family name: Leguminosae. A family is a collection of related genera (plural of genus).

To go further, families of plants with some similarities are grouped into *orders*. Orders are grouped into *subclasses* and *classes*. Classes are grouped into *phyla*. Each grouping is larger and includes more plants than the one that precedes it.

So, in the terms used today, the whole classification of the white clover, going from the largest grouping to the smallest, is as follows:

Phylum — Spermatophyta
Class — Angiospermae
Subclass — Dicotyledoneae
Order — Rosales
Family — Leguminosae
Genus — *Trifolium*
Species — *Repens*
(Scientific name, *Trifolium repens*)

Such an arrangement of plants, when it is accompanied by the descriptions that go with each grouping, provides a means by which a person can find his way around in the plant world and can identify and name the plants he encounters.

Before Linnaeus' day many attempts had been made at arranging plants in groups so as to identify them. There had been groupings by alphabetical name, but often there were many names for one plant, and besides, if a person did not already know the name, he had little chance of finding the plant in an alphabetical system — short of going through the entire list.

Plants had also been grouped by time of flowering or by place of growth or by their medicinal uses, but these factors were so variable that no good arrangement could be made by using them. Other ways of arranging plants have been based on their general appearance, their roots, leaves, flowers, or fruits, or on combinations of these.

Konrad von Gesner (1516–65), a Swiss naturalist, seems to have been the first person really to make a step toward a scientific classification when he touched on the subject of arranging genera according to their fruits.

Andrea Cesalpino (1519–1603), an Italian botanist, went much farther in arranging plants in a truly systematic manner, classifying them according to their parts of fructification in his work, *De Plantis*. All the classifiers who followed him, including Linnaeus, were indebted to Cesalpino and his ideas.

Several systems were based on plant flowers. Tournefort carried this arrangement the furthest, putting plants into classes according to the form of their flower and putting them into orders according to the situation of the fruit on the plant. There were many uncertainties in his method, however.

Linnaeus, taking a hint from Vaillant, was the first to put forward a complete system that classified plants according to the stamens and pistils of their flowers. While it was far from perfect, his system was simple and easy to remember and it was based on the parts of the plant that probably varied the least and could therefore be recognized most readily.

He first published his method of plant classification in 1735, in *Systema Naturae* (*A System of Nature*). In this book, Linnaeus briefly arranged in charts and described the three kingdoms of nature: plant, animal, and mineral. It is the plant kingdom that concerns us here. He grouped plants into twenty-four *classes* distinguished by the number, proportion, or situation of the stamens. The plant classes were divided into *orders* depending on the number or differences of the pistils, the florets (individual small flowers), or some other parts. The plant orders were in turn divided into *genera* according to the form of the fruits.

The classes of plants were as follows:

I. Monandria (one male) — 1 stamen, or male part, in each flower, which also contains the female parts.

II. Diandria (two males) — 2 distinct stamens in each flower, which also contains the female parts.

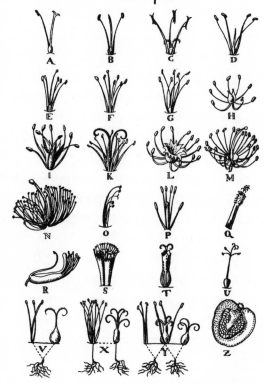

Clarisſ: LINNÆI.M.D.
METHODUS plantarum SEXUALIS
in SISTEMATE NATURÆ
deſcripta

Lugd. bat: *1736*

G.D. EHRET. Palat-heidelb:
fecit & edidit

Drawing made in 1736, to illustrate Linnaeus' system of
classification. A. Monandria, B. Diandria. C. Triandria.
D. Tetrandria. E. Pentandria. F. Hexandria. G. Heptandria.
H. Octandria. I. Enneandria. K. Decandria. L. Dodecandria.
M. Icosandria. N. Polyandria. O. Didynamia. P. Tetradynamia.
Q. Monodelphia. R. Diadelphia. S. Polyadelphia. T. Syngenesia.
U. Gynandria. V. Monoecia. X. Dioecia Y. Polygamia.
Z. Cryptogamia. For an explanation of these terms, see the list
of Linnaeus' classes.

III. Triandria (three males) — 3 distinct stamens in each flower, which also contains the female parts.

IV. Tetrandria (four males) — 4 distinct stamens in each flower, which also contains the female parts.

V. Pentandria (five males) — 5 distinct stamens in each flower, which also contains the female parts.

VI. Hexandria (six males) — 6 distinct stamens in each flower, which also contains the female parts.

VII. Heptandria (seven males) — 7 distinct stamens in each flower, which also contains the female parts.

VIII. Octandria (eight males) — 8 distinct stamens in each flower, which also contains the female parts.

IX. Enneandria (nine males) — 9 distinct stamens in each flower, which also contains the female parts.

X. Decandria (ten males) — 10 distinct stamens in each flower, which also contains the female parts.

XI. Dodecandria (twelve males) — From 12 to 19 distinct stamens in each flower, which also contains the female parts.

XII. Icosandria (20 males) — More than 12 distinct stamens in each flower, fixed on the calyx or petals and not on the receptacle.

XIII. Polyandria (many males) — From 20 to 1,000 distinct stamens in each flower, fixed on the receptacle.

XIV. Didynamia (two powers) — 4 distinct stamens in each flower, two of which are longer than the other two. Female parts in the same flower.

XV. Tetradynamia (four powers) — 6 distinct stamens in each flower, four of which are longer than the other two. Female parts in the same flower.

XVI. Monodelphia (one brotherhood) — All the stamens united by their filaments into one body.

XVII. Diadelphia (two brotherhoods) — Stamens united by their filaments into one or two sets.

XVIII. Polyadelphia (many brotherhoods) — Stamens united by their filaments into three or more sets.

XIX. Syngenesia (confederate males) — 5 stamens, united by their anthers into a cylinder.

XX. Gynandria (feminine males) — Stamens inserted in the pistil.

XXI. Monoecia (one house) — Stamens (males) and pistils (females) on the same plant, but in distinct flowers.

XXII. Dioecia (two houses) — Stamens and pistils on separate plants.

XXIII. Polygamia (polygamies) — Hermaphrodite flowers and male or female flowers (or both) on the same plants. (Hermaphrodite flowers are those that have both stamen and pistil in the same bloom.)

XXIV. Cryptogamia (secret marriages) — Methods of forming fruit concealed.

These characteristics were fairly easy to observe and furnished a means of sorting the plants out. Inevitably some plants that were not closely related ended up in the same group, for this was a purely artificial system of classification, having little to do with true plant relationships, about which comparatively little was known in Linnaeus' day. The system was an important step in establishing order in the botanical world, however.

Probably as valuable as his classification method was Linnaeus' attempt to establish certain working rules and guiding principles to be followed in the classification and naming of plants — something that was badly needed. In *Fundamenta Botanica* (*Botanical Foundations*), published in 1736, and in greater detail in *Critica Botanica* (*Botanical Opinions*), published in 1737, Linnaeus set forth many of his rules. It is astonishing to note how many of them are still recognized as sound and are followed by botanists today.

In a preface to *Critica Botanica*, Linnaeus wrote especially of plant names, saying that he found "hardly any [botanists] who have attempted to develop nomenclature, one of the two foundations of botany, though that a name should remain unshaken is quite as essential as attention to genera. . . . There is so much disagreement between the authorities that the reader can hardly determine to which in preference to the others he should give allegiance, since satisfactory principles are not anywhere to be seen. Wherefore it is not surprising if when the novice has developed into a mature botanist, appearing the while to have done all that was possible, he in his work makes mistakes over nomenclature and so comes to burden botany with wrong names.

"Wherefore we can never hope for a lasting peace and better times till botanists come to an agreement among themselves about the fixed laws in accordance with which judgment can be pronounced on names; that is to say, good names can be absolutely distinguished from bad ones, the good ones maintained and the bad ones banished without any exception, so that botany firmly built on immovable principles may remain a fortress inviolable and unshaken.

"Before botanists can admit such laws, it is necessary that someone among them should take upon himself to offer proposals to be examined by other botanists, so that if they are good they may be confirmed; if unsound they may be convicted of unsoundness and abandoned, while something better is put in their place. So long as botanists refuse to make this beginning, so long also will they remain in doubt and uncertainty, and false names will accumulate every day to burden botany. Now, as hitherto no one has thought fit to undertake this self-denying task, I have determined to make the attempt. . . . I have not reached such an extreme of hardihood as to believe that all my reasoning is so firmly based but that someone else may propound reasoning much more mature: still mine will be true until some other principles are shown to be truer."

He then went on to give his rules. Many of them are sensible and seem self-evident today.

The foundation of all classification of plants depends on genera and species, he wrote. A botanist should use care and judgment in selecting a name for a new-found plant and should not merely give it the name that first occurs to him.

All those plants that belong to different genera must be designated by different generic names. There shall be only one generic name where one and the same genus is concerned.

If one and the same generic name has been adopted for two different genera, one of the names must be changed.

Linnaeus went on to tell of his personal woes with this problem, saying that when he was a young man following closely in the footsteps of the botanists Tournefort and Rivinus, "I suffered grievous torture as I changed from one treatise and method to another, and back again. For *Aconitum, Angelica,* and others, as I met them in the fields of Rivinus were no longer the same plants that I had previously gathered in the fields of Tournefort. A name which had been fixed in my memory associated with some particular genus had presently to be expunged and to occupy a different position. This sudden shifting could hardly be managed without confusion: and perhaps the reader may recognize that I am not the only one who has suffered from such confusion."

Still on the subject of generic names, Linnaeus wrote that the same genus must bear the same name in any system, no matter how much the systems differ. He who establishes a new genus should give it a name, and an unchangeable generic name must be fixed before any specific name is devised.

"I beseech you to have distinct genera, distinct ideas, distinct names," he wrote. "If you introduce confusion in names, ideas are confounded, and so are genera; and if these are confounded, there is confusion everywhere."

The best generic names are those that show the plant's essential character or its appearance.

"It is a distinguishing mark of a very good name that the plant should offer its hand to the name and the name should grasp the plant by the hand; if they are connected so closely that they can hardly be separated, assuredly they ought not to be," he wrote.

As an example, Linnaeus mentioned *Helianthus,*

which means "flower of the sun," or "sunflower." "Who can see this plant in flower, whose great golden blossoms send out rays in every direction from the circular disk, without admiring the handsome flower modeled on the sun's shape? And as one admires, presently the name occurs to the mind, even as, if one sees only the name, the admired picture of the flower comes before one."

Linnaeus recommended that the old Greek and Latin names be kept as generic terms, and he approved of names taken from poetry or mythology, or of names commemorating kings and famous botanists. He rejected some of the picturesque and lovely religious names, however. *Pater noster* (our Father), *Gratia dei* (Grace of God), *Lacryma Jobi* (Job's tears), and similar names should no longer be used, he said.

As to specific names, Linnaeus said, "The specific name is nothing else than a primary characteristic taken from the diagnosis, by means of which I can distinguish this species from all others of the same genus, speedily, safely, pleasantly.

"The diagnosis is a description of all parts of the plant according to their number, shape, position, and proportion, taking account of those characteristics alone which occur in no other species of the same genus."

As far as possible, a specific name should indicate a characteristic difference that makes a plant unique and is appropriate only to that species. The shorter a specific name, the better — if such a name can be found.

These and many other rules appeared in *Critica Botanica*. Some of Linnaeus' colleagues renounced them, but other botanists, recognizing the problems facing their science, welcomed the suggestions for reform.

Another important work of Linnaeus' was *Genera Plantarum* (*The Genera of Plants*), also published in 1737. In this book, Linnaeus described every genus of plant then known; he also introduced a new classification whereby the genera could easily be identified and the name of each determined.

In Holland also, *Flora Lapponica* (*Lapland Flora*), on which Linnaeus had worked since his Lapland journey, was finally published in 1737.

Add to this, *Hortus Cliffortianus, Classes Plantarum*, Artedi's *Ichthyologia*, and five or six other works of Linnaeus' own, and the astonishment at his output grows. These were substantial books, not the airy musings of a light-minded man. True, some of the work was hasty; even Linnaeus knew that it was not all perfect and that it might in time be superseded by something better. But he also was well aware that someone had to take the first step: the accumulated knowledge of past botanists must be sorted and arranged; the worthwhile must be rescued and put in some sort of order; the worthless must be discarded; changes must be made where necessary; suggestions for future procedures must be put forward. Linnaeus was willing to do this task; the books of his Holland years stand as a monument to his youthful dedication and industry.

Now the Holland years were over, and Linnaeus faced a new career as a physician in his native Sweden.

DR. LINNAEUS OF STOCKHOLM

ARRIVING IN STOCKHOLM IN 1738, CARL
Linnaeus was to receive a rude jolt. In Holland
he had lived among a circle of admiring friends
as a recognized man of science, doing serious
work. In France and England he had been received as a coming young botanist who had fresh
and interesting ideas and had written a number
of promising books. Although other botanists
might not always agree with him, they were will-

ing to admit that he was a brilliant and stimulating thinker, and they accepted him, for the most part, with the courtesy due such a man. In Stockholm he was ignored or, worse still, ridiculed.

Later, Linnaeus wrote a friend, "I settled in Stockholm and was the laughingstock of everybody on account of my botany. No one cared how many restless nights and toilsome hours I had put into it. . . . I began to set up for a practitioner, but my success was very slow. No one would even put a servant under my care." The fame that Linnaeus had known in other countries was completely lacking in Sweden. To the residents of Stockholm he was merely one more beginning doctor seeking to establish a practice.

Again, as he had in earlier years, Linnaeus went through a time of poverty and discouragement. But he was resilient and resourceful, and proved to be an astute physician who was well ahead of his time in many of his ideas about infection and the causes of disease. Gradually he became known for his success in treating lung troubles and fevers.

Sheer luck played its part in his career, too. One day he prescribed for the cough of a lady who frequently appeared at the royal court. Soon after, this lady was seized with a fit of coughing in the presence of Queen Ulrika Eleonora, who herself was troubled with a cough. When the queen saw the lady ease her attack by putting a tablet into her mouth, she inquired about the remedy.

As a result, Linnaeus was called to court. He prescribed the same tablets for the queen, and in consequence her ailment disappeared. With this episode, Linnaeus was on his way to becoming a popular and fashionable physician, sought after by the wealthy and the powerful. By the end of 1739 he had almost more patients than he could attend to.

Count Karl Gustaf Tessin, Speaker of the Swedish Parliament's House of Nobles, was keenly interested in science, and in time he heard of Linnaeus' fame abroad. Tessin sought to do some favor for the young botanist who had advanced Sweden's name so much in other countries. One of Linnaeus' acquaintances had recently resigned as lecturer on assaying and mineralogy for the ore collection belonging to Sweden's Board of Mines, at the Royal College. He suggested that Linnaeus ask Tessin for the appointment to this post. Tessin was glad to oblige, provided that Linnaeus would also give lectures on botany during the summer.

In addition, Tessin offered Linnaeus a room in his house and invited him to eat at Tessin's own table. Here the botanist had the opportunity to meet many men who ranked high in the government. But Tessin went even further. The office of Physician to the Navy in Stockholm became vacant, and Tessin obtained the appointment for Linnaeus.

Now that the botanist had become known, he joined with other interested men in Stockholm to form the

Carl Linnaeus, holding a sprig of *Linnaea borealis*.

Academy of Science. The first president of this scientific society was chosen by lot, and Linnaeus drew the lucky ballot. So, within one month he had become president of the Stockholm Academy of Science, public lecturer on ores, and Physician to the Navy, besides increasing his own private medical practice. Even Dr. Moraeus could no longer have any doubts about the future of his would-be son-in-law, and in June, 1739, Linnaeus journeyed to Falun where his marriage to Sara Elizabeth took place.

After a month's vacation at Falun, Linnaeus returned to Stockholm and his medical duties, while Sara Elizabeth remained with her parents. In Stockholm his work caught him up again. At the naval hospital, with only the help of a surgeon and an under-surgeon, he visited between one and two hundred patients a day. All the time, the number of his private patients was increasing.

Yet always in his mind his first love, botany, lingered. Busy as he was, he somehow found time to start laying out a botanical garden for the growing of plants used in medicine. He devoted many hours to preparing his lectures for the Royal College, and in connection with his botany talks he invited his listeners to go with him on field trips around the meadows and parks of Stockholm after church on Sunday afternoons. As had happened years before when Linnaeus had given the botanical lectures at Uppsala, his public was delighted with his lively and colorful way of speaking, and soon he had a crowd of listeners. But he still dreamed of Uppsala and of teaching there. "If I could go to Uppsala," he wrote a friend, "I would give up entirely the practice of medicine and devote my whole attention to plants."

In January, 1740, his first child, Carl, was born. Linnaeus was overjoyed to have a son, but was far too occupied in Stockholm to go to Falun to visit his family.

That same year, in the spring, Professor Rudbeck died, leaving vacant the position of teacher of botany at Uppsala. Here might be the golden opportunity! Full of hope, Linnaeus asked Tessin to use whatever influence he had, to obtain the position for him. Tessin wrote the chancellor of the university in Linnaeus' behalf, but Rosén, already on the scene, had also applied for the post. Even Linnaeus had to admit that it was only fair that his rival, Rosén, should be first choice and should be awarded the position.

But a different opportunity soon presented itself to Linnaeus. In the early months of 1741 the Swedish Diet had spent considerable thought on trying to promote ways whereby Sweden's economic condition might be improved. One recommendation had been to cut down on imports and find a greater use for Sweden's own raw materials. There was a great deal of interest in exploring the various provinces with a careful eye to seeing exactly what their natural resources might be. Such an undertaking had never been attempted, and some parts of Sweden were still largely unknown to any but their own inhabitants. It had been suggested that Linnaeus might make a journey through the south of Sweden similar to his tours of Lapland and Dalarna. The members of the Diet who had heard him lecture in Stockholm were confident of his ability to do this.

Accordingly, Linnaeus was offered the chance to travel through Sweden's islands of Öland, Västergotland, and Gotland at government expense. He was given particular instructions to look for all plants and minerals that might be suitable for dyeing and other domestic manufactures; to search for plants that might be used for medicines at home and abroad; and to watch out for any clay soils that might be proper for making porcelain ware. In addition, he was to take general note of the plants, minerals, and animals of the area, as he had in Lapland.

He was delighted to accept the offer, and chose six young men to accompany him as assistants. The group left Stockholm in the middle of May, 1741, bound for the port of Kalmar, where they were to take passage for the island of Öland. Since Växjö lay on the route to Kalmar, Linnaeus and his companions stopped to see Dr. Rothman. The small truant of grammar school days had fulfilled the promise his teacher had seen in him, Dr. Rothman was happy to observe.

At Kalmar, Linnaeus encountered his old enemy, bad weather, and he and the members of his party were forced to stay at the port for several days before they could cross over to Öland. Finding a place where they might eat was difficult, but the apothecary at Kalmar finally gave them food and shelter.

At last they decided to chance the voyage — a rough one. They stayed overnight at the place where they landed on Öland, then proceeded slowly on foot, collecting plants as they went. Linnaeus was amazed at the great numbers of wild orchis flowers he saw. They were the same kinds he had seen growing in the gardens at Fontainebleau in France. The winter before his trip to Öland he had written to Spain to ask for some of these orchis plants for his garden, never dreaming that they grew wild in his own native Sweden.

"The country is splendidly green hereabout; the houses are thatched with birch bark and straw," wrote Linnaeus. "Hence we went to Smedby, and from here to Möckleby, where the alum slate quarries are. Here I had the mishap to crush my left foot with a great stone falling from a wall, and was compelled to lie up for a while at the inn at Möckleby until able to get on to Ahlbrunnedy at Ottenby, in the southern end of the island. Here we found the people pretty considerably alarmed at us and at our travels, so that we were in a manner obliged to go on to the inn at Näsby. Most of us stayed the night with the co-minister at Åhs, where we rested through Sunday.

"As we left the chaplain at Åhs, people came following us out of the village to look upon us as a curiosity.

... The sea birds were various and numerous.

"Next morning [June 9] we went down to the beach, which was one-eighth of a mile from Hillterstad. The dew lay on the grass, and the lark trilled deliciously."

On the beach the group looked for seaweeds and pebbles. All this searching did not go unobserved. There had been rumors of war with Russia, and soon the story spread through the island that Linnaeus and his party were spies. Wherever they went, the Ölanders regarded them with deep suspicion, until finally the travelers took a government employee along with them to give themselves the proper air of officialdom and authority.

"Rye is the grain most grown here; barley does not thrive well, the soil being so sandy," wrote Linnaeus in his miscellaneous notes. "About here is the best cornland in the islands. The roe deer betakes itself mostly to the northern end of Öland, the fallow deer to the southern part. Wild swine are not uncommon in the northern part, doing the farmer considerable damage. Much wood is brought here from Småland. The women busy themselves with stocking knitting."

On June 16 the party wished to go on to the island of Gotland, but again the old bugaboo, bad weather, intervened. Five days went by before they could make the crossing. They landed at Visby, the only town on Gotland, at two o'clock in the afternoon on June 21.

Visby had been the great market center of western Europe during the twelfth and thirteenth centuries. A large part of the Eastern trade that normally went through Constantinople or Egypt had been rerouted north during the disturbed state of affairs in the East that had led up to the Crusades. The trade route had stretched through Russia, then down the Baltic Sea to Visby. The town had flourished for two centuries, until the cities of the Hanseatic League became powerful. In 1361, King Waldemar IV of Denmark had finally taken it by storm, and its many churches had been ruined.

"This town looked to us like a model of Rome, so splendid is it, with its many great roofless churches, which time has ruined, and its strong and lofty walls of hewn stone," wrote Linnaeus.

"It occupies a half circle on the slope of a steep hill. It is not very large, being enclosed and fortified on the land side with a high wall and many strong towers."

On Gotland the group traveled by horse. Linnaeus wrote on June 27: "Up at four to read a runic stone by the churchyard; then we botanized on cliff and coast in the creek or bay of Capell, studying the corals, here very rich. We came at eight to Hau, which is indisputably the prettiest farmhouse in the kingdom. It is bordered by the sea and a little brook on two sides; on the two others by tall and steep chalk cliffs. A long rhyming description was traced on the woodwork of the courtyard. This house has no neighbors within half a mile.

"From Hau we passed on next day to Rilka, where there are plenty of plants. An unknown bird shrieked at us with an unusually strong voice."

On June 28 the party went to Fårö, an island near Gotland, where there were "seals and porpoises in plenty." Of seal catching, Linnaeus noted that "seal-stones are large, flat, broad stones that lie along the shore and come scarcely above the surface of the sea. Where they do not occur naturally, the fishermen set them out. A net is placed to form a half circle on the seaward side of the stone. When a seal wishes to sleep or rest, he must seek out such a stone, and he always climbs up onto it from the shoreward side. He then rests with his nose turned seaward, so that if he is frightened he can quickly dive into the sea, and thus he comes into the net." The explorers also noted how profitably whaling and salmon fishing were carried on here. During the two nights of their stay they slept in the Fårö church for want of any other place.

Back in Gotland on June 30, they traveled southward through a forest that was being cut down by limeburners for their kilns. "The numerous peat bogs are jestingly called Gotland's gold mines," wrote Linnaeus. "Another source of wealth is the eiderdown. The feathers lining the nest are gray, with white spots. The bird tears the down out of herself when she broods, and covers the eggs with it; it is, however, mixed with moss and brushwood."

Still going south, the travelers visited many offshore islands. Of Gotland, Linnaeus wrote: "We noticed in this country a great calmness in people's aims and objects in life, especially in regard to public business transactions. Newspapers come very seldom, and few persons seem interested in public affairs."

On one small offshore island the journeyers passed the night in a fisherman's hut, for no one else lived on the island. Its scanty, salt-sprayed grass was cropped closely by sheep.

The group arrived back at Visby on July 17, and two days later returned to Öland. On July 27 they made the passage back to Kalmar on the mainland. Västergotland, their third objective, was left out, because time had grown short.

Linnaeus returned to Stockholm by way of Växjö, Stenbrohult, and Uppsala, arriving back at the capital on August 29, 1741. His trip had been a valuable one for Sweden; he had found out much that was to prove useful for the development of the country. His discoveries in minerals and zoology were important, and he had made a catalog of one hundred plants that for the first time had been found to be natives of Sweden.

Roberg had finally resigned at Uppsala, and the professorship of medicine and anatomy had become vacant. The chancellor of the university, knowing Linnaeus' anxiety for a teaching post, helped him obtain the position although there were rivals for it. Linnaeus moved his family to Uppsala in the fall of 1741.

Actually, although he had finally achieved his heart's

desire and was back at Uppsala, he was not as well off financially as before. In Stockholm he had become a well-known and prosperous doctor. In Uppsala he was to receive only the salary of an assistant professor for the time being, since Roberg was to have his full salary until his death. Fortunately, Sara Elizabeth had money of her own, and the family could live moderately well until Linnaeus eventually received the amount that Roberg was getting.

Linnaeus was inducted into his position on October 23, 1741. It was a great day for him — the fulfillment of his fondest dreams. By a long route he had come back to Uppsala.

Remembering his wit and liveliness as a speaker, crowds flocked to hear his inaugural address. His speech, "Concerning the Necessity of Travels within One's Native Land," was concerned with his experiences in Lapland and Gotland and stated the economic value to Sweden of expeditions such as his.

There was still one slight cloud, however. He would have liked to teach botany, but Rosén held that professorship, although by training he was a teacher of medicine and anatomy. Accordingly, early in 1742, by mutual agreement and with the approval of the chancellor of the university, an exchange was arranged. It was settled that Rosén should teach anatomy, physiology, pathology, diagnostics, and medical practice. Linnaeus was to teach botany, natural history, mineralogy, zoology, pharmacy, chemistry, and dietetics. His title was to be Professor of Medicine and Botany.

Linnaeus was now almost thirty-five years old. He had achieved his long-sought goal, and his happiness was complete.

HOME TO UPPSALA

LINNAEUS RETURNED TO UPPSALA WITH THE
feeling of coming home again — home to botany
and home to a place he knew and loved. He had
left Uppsala as a somewhat insecure and discon-
tented young man going out into the world to
better himself. Away from Uppsala he had won
his medical degree, published his manuscripts,
gained a wealth of knowledge and experience,
established a reputation, and made many friends

among scientific men. Now, for the most part, his adventures were over. He had reached a turning point and was ready to settle down to the life of a writer, a scholar, a teacher, a man with a family.

Never again would he have quite the eagerness or the headlong impetuosity of his Lapland and Holland years — he was older now. For him, the nightingale had ceased to "sing all the way."

But never would he lose his sense of wonder and his burning curiosity to know everything possible about the natural world around him. Always his eyes would sparkle and his face light up at the sight of a flower he did not know, a bird he had not seen before, an insect that was somehow different. His love of plants and animals was so genuine and so spontaneous that no one who heard him lecture could ever forget his magic. Years after they had left Uppsala his pupils were to remember him and boast of having "studied with Linnaeus."

Now, as professor of botany, he gave up the practice of medicine except for attending some of his friends and the poor people who otherwise might not have had the care they needed.

The old stone house where he had lived with the Rudbecks was in terrible disrepair and, Linnaeus said, was "like an owl's nest." In 1742 this house was rebuilt for him; the rooms and windows were made larger and the ceilings were plastered. Linnaeus lived here rent free for the rest of his life. The nearness of the house to the

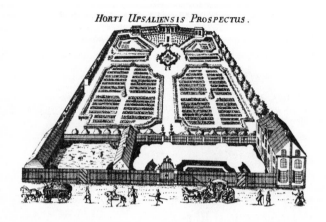

HORTI UPSALIENSIS PROSPECTUS.

A drawing of the Uppsala garden in 1745, as reorganized by Linnaeus. The greenhouses are at the left. At the right is the old Rudbeck house, where Linnaeus lived for many years.

botanical garden made it an ideal dwelling for him.

The garden was still in disgraceful condition. The damage done in the fire of 1702 had never been wholly repaired, the greenhouses had not been rebuilt, and the plants had otherwise been badly neglected. As professor of botany, Linnaeus was in charge of the garden — a circumstance that he viewed with satisfaction. He immediately set about drawing up plans to make the botanical garden everything it should be. He asked the university for new greenhouses, and his request was granted. One of his friends at the royal court made sketches for the tropical planthouse and for a new layout of the whole garden. When work was completed, Linnaeus fell to, writing his friends in France, Holland,

and England and asking them to help him by sending whatever rare plants they could. Soon parcels of seeds began arriving at Uppsala.

Now an experienced head gardener was needed, for many of the new plants were unusual and were not such as ordinarily grew in a northern climate. They would need special attention from a seasoned plant expert.

For the position, Linnaeus knew just the man — Dietrich Nietzel, whom he remembered from his days at Hartecamp, in Holland. Nietzel accepted Linnaeus' offer and stayed at Uppsala until his death in 1756. Linnaeus valued his work highly and depended on his good judgment to make the garden flourish.

Between 1742 and 1744, about one thousand different species of seeds were sent Linnaeus by his friends, and visitors arrived with living plant specimens. In 1748, six years after Linnaeus began his work with the garden, he published a description of it. Listed among the plants growing at Uppsala were eleven hundred species from foreign countries — an amazing number for those days.

The garden had a fascination for Linnaeus, but it was, after all, only an instrument to be used in his main work, teaching. Into that, Linnaeus entered wholeheartedly. Besides public lectures, a certain amount of private tutoring was expected of each professor. To this, Linnaeus gave far more of himself than was demanded, although, it is true, his wealthier students paid him well.

To Uppsala, Linnaeus was like a fresh and revitalizing breeze after a muggy day. Under Rudbeck and Roberg, both aged, teaching had fallen into the doldrums. Now here was a young man, in his thirties only, vigorous and full of enthusiasm for his subject. The students' interest was immediately sparked; they found his wit and energy captivating, and admired his knowledge, his thoroughness, his wonderful memory, and the clearness with which he could develop an idea.

Listeners crowded his lectures. In winter the talks took place in one of the lecture halls, but in spring and autumn in the botanical garden or the zoological museum. Besides these lectures, Linnaeus inaugurated a series of natural history expeditions at the end of the spring and the beginning of the fall terms. These expeditions were to become famous. Sometimes between two and three hundred students joined them.

The members of the expeditions would start out in the morning, fanning out over the countryside to collect the insects, the plants, and the birds that might arouse their interest. A series of meeting places were arranged beforehand, and when the students had assembled at these points, Linnaeus would lecture on whatever they had found that was unusual, drawing his listeners about him as he pointed to a strange leaf, an almost unnoticeable flower, or an odd marking on a butterfly. Chores were assigned to various members of the expedition. One took notes on the lectures; another attended to discipline so that everything might be done in an orderly way.

Gradually the members of Linnaeus' expeditions adopted a sort of uniform — linen trousers and jackets. Some of the students carried butterfly nets; others had cases for pressing plant specimens. All through the long day they roamed the fields and woods — a throng of jolly, laughing youths. In the evening, at about nine o'clock, they trooped back together into Uppsala, tired but still carefree, some of them wearing wreaths of flowers, and others sporting flowers on their hats. Somewhere along the line of march a kettledrum would join in, French horns would sound, and banners would be unfurled. Now in procession, the students would approach the botanical garden. There they would stop in the approaching dusk, before disbanding, and a cheer would go up: *"Vivat scientia! Vivat Linnaeus!"* ("Long live science! Long live Linnaeus!") For many a famous botanist that cry from his student days was to echo in his memory all through his life.

Now, for Linnaeus, there began a period of intense writing activity. In 1745 he published *Öland and Gotland Journey*, an account of his travels in those islands. Later in the same year, *Flora Suecica* (*The Plants of Sweden*) appeared, to be followed in 1746 by *Fauna Suecica* (*The Animals of Sweden*). Both these books were highly valuable, as at the time there was little general knowledge of the plants and animals native to the country. Of the book on plants, Linnaeus wrote that before he could complete it he "was obliged to travel through most of the provinces of the kingdom, and even walk through Lapland, a country uncultivated and with few beaten roads; and he was everywhere put to incredible trouble in searching for plants." In writing of the animal book, he mentioned the "endless and incredible energy" needed to have been able to collect so many animals, particularly insects.

In the spring of 1746, Linnaeus also undertook the journey to Västergotland that had been omitted at the time of the Öland and Gotland tour. This time he traveled with only one companion, who acted as a secretary.

Linnaeus firmly held the view that "the only good naturalist is a traveling naturalist." In 1746, with the help of Count Tessin, he reached an agreement with the East India Company by which he was enabled to send some of his most promising young students out across the world to explore and send back plants. By the arrangement the company would make an annual grant for the purpose of research in natural history to any one student who cared to accept it, provided he was approved by Linnaeus. The grant gave free passage to and from any country to which the East India Company's ships might go. The young men who sailed out on botanical missions came to be known by Linnaeus as his apostles. A roster of them includes some of the famous names in the annals of botany.

Home to Uppsala

The first of the apostles was Christopher Ternström, who headed for the Far East. Linnaeus sent him off with a long list of instructions concerning things to observe and specimens to collect. For himself, Linnaeus longed for a small growing tea bush or, if nothing else, some seeds of the tea plant. For her Majesty the Queen, whom Linnaeus was helping with her natural history collection, Linnaeus asked for some living goldfish. But at a group of islands off the coast of Cambodia the ship was delayed by a storm. There Ternström died, the first of several apostles who were to lose their lives on their botanical missions far from home.

During 1747, Linnaeus busied himself with writing *Flora Zeylanica* (*The Flora of Ceylon*). The material for this book came from a collection of dried specimens that had been made by a Dutchman, Paul Hermann, who had gone out to Ceylon with the Dutch East India Company in the seventeenth century. Upon his return he had busied himself with classifying his specimens, but had died before he finished the work. In some way the plant collection had disappeared. Years later it turned up in Copenhagen, Denmark. The apothecary who came upon it knew he had something unusual and returned it to Holland to find out what it was. He was referred to Linnaeus, to whom the collection was sent at Uppsala.

Linnaeus had known of the existence of Hermann's Ceylon herbarium and recognized it at once. He was delighted, for a group of strange plants like this was his

149

greatest joy. The collection was loaned to him and he set to work immediately, laboring day and night, examining, sorting, describing, naming. As he himself noted, because of the length of time the plants had been dried, they were difficult to work with, and his task was almost a Herculean one. *Flora Zeylanica* was finished and published the next year.

For a long time now, Linnaeus and some of his fellow scientists had been urging that Swedish naturalists be sent on an expedition to North America, to ship back seeds and plants that might also be grown in their own country. In 1747, one of Linnaeus' most promising students, Peter Kalm, was chosen for the mission. He was a young Finn who had already been on a plant-collecting journey to Russia.

Kalm left in October, 1747, taking with him a trained gardener to help in packing and sending live plants and in collecting seeds. Adverse winds hindered sailing so badly that the two did not reach America for almost a year. There, starting at Philadelphia, Kalm and his companion journeyed through Pennsylvania, New Jersey, and New York. Then they went up the Hudson River and across the Great Lakes into Canada, traveling much of the time in wilderness territory. They returned to Sweden in July, 1751, bringing with them a magnificent collection of plant specimens and seeds.

Linnaeus already had some knowledge of North American plants and owned some specimens that had been sent him direct or through English collectors or his friend Gronovius, in Holland. But he was more than eager to see what Kalm had brought back. He had been ill during parts of 1750 and 1751. When Kalm arrived with his wonderful collection, however, Linnaeus "got up and recovered, through pleasure at the sight of the plants."

Meanwhile, in 1749, Linnaeus had made a tour of the province of Skåne, reporting, as before in other provinces, on the plants, the animals, the natural resources, and the economic possibilities of the area.

Also in 1749, Fredrik Hasselquist, one of Linnaeus' apostles, left for Egypt. Hasselquist was a brilliant young man of great promise, but his health was poor and he had no money. Possibly he never should have undertaken his journey. Linnaeus, feeling a little apprehensive, had warned him of its perils and problems, and also of the costs of such a trip. But, since Hasselquist was determined to go and had a relative in Smyrna with whom he could stay for part of the time, Linnaeus consented to help him obtain a grant for his expenses. After five months in Smyrna, Hasselquist wrote that the money had been spent, and again Linnaeus raised a sum to help him, partly by a grant, partly by personal contributions which Linnaeus collected from his friends. Upon receiving the money, Hasselquist went on to Palestine, Arabia, Cyprus, and Rhodes. He finally returned to Smyrna with a large and very fine collection of plants, and there he died in 1752, over two years after he had left Sweden.

Linnaeus was saddened by the death of his young friend and he was ridden with anxiety that all Hasselquist's work would have gone for nothing. The young man had incurred many debts and unless they could be paid there was no hope of recovering his plant collection. Linnaeus spent months in worrying and seeking for a solution to the problem. Finally the queen, who felt a great fondness for her botanical adviser, bought the collection and Hasselquist's journal. Linnaeus was enchanted with this journal and, by order of the queen, set about editing it.

In 1750, two more of Linnaeus' apostles went abroad: Peter Osbeck to China as a pastor, and Peter Löfling, whom Linnaeus considered his best pupil, to travel through Spain.

In 1751, *Philosophia Botanica* (*Botanical Philosophy*) was published. Linnaeus had possessed this in manuscript form for some time. Many of his friends who knew its value had urged him to have it printed so that botanists everywhere might benefit from it. The book was a general survey of the field of botany. It gave a short review of the principal botanists and their systems and explained the different parts of plants. It showed by examples what the characters of the different classes and orders were, how to tell the common species from the subdivisions with slight differences, called varieties, how to describe them accurately, and how to arrange them correctly. It ended with advice to young botanists on how to prepare an herbarium, establish a botanical garden, and carry out an expedition. It was a compendium of knowledge important to any botanist and is still considered to contain good basic material.

From 1751 on, Linnaeus made frequent trips to the royal court in Stockholm. Crown Prince Adolphus Frederick had now become king. Both he and his wife, Queen Louisa Ulrica, were great natural history enthusiasts. Like many people of the day, they collected natural history objects. They depended on Linnaeus to help them name their specimens correctly and arrange the royal collections. Linnaeus enjoyed talking with his king and queen, but the ceremony and artificiality of the court were trying to a person of his abrupt and forthright nature. The queen, especially, found great amusement in his directness of manner.

At this time he was working on one of his most important books, *Species Plantarum* (*The Species of Plants*). In it he attempted to describe all the species of plants that were known at the time, insofar as that was possible. Since his collection of dried and living plants was now huge and had come to him from many parts of the world, no one had better material for this work than he. It was a stupendous task. Linnaeus was now over forty, and his years of unceasing labor were beginning to tell on him. His formerly cheerful nature had given way to moods of depression and suspicion, and he suffered from a variety of ailments. But Linnaeus without work would not have been Linnaeus at all, so on he toiled.

To add to his troubles, Rosén had been appointed president of the College of Medicine and also physician to the king, so he was often absent from the university. This meant that Linnaeus must act as his deputy at Uppsala. Unquestionably there were times when the extra work was a burden.

But there were happy times, too. On Christmas Day, 1752, he received some cherished presents. From the queen came a gold ring set with a ruby, and from Count Tessin a gold watch and a valuable book on plants.

Linnaeus' former students were doing well, and that was a source of satisfaction to him, also. Löfling sent him plant specimens from Spain. Moreover, King Ferdinand VI of Spain was so pleased with Löfling's work that he had arranged for the young botanist to travel in South America to collect specimens for the Spanish monarch, the King of France, the Queen of Sweden, and Linnaeus. Naturally Linnaeus was pleased to hear himself mentioned in the same breath with so much royalty, but more than that he looked forward to receiving new plants.

Work was going forward on *Species Plantarum*, and Osbeck arrived back from China at this time too, with six hundred plant specimens. He sent them all to Linnaeus.

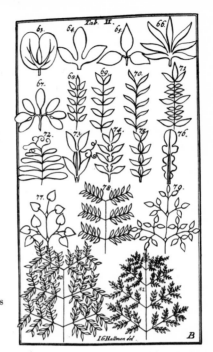

Types of compound leaves, as
illustrated by Linnaeus'
Philosophia Botanica.

Species Plantarum was published in 1753. In it, Linnaeus described 7,300 species of plants. This was a goodly number for that day. The work was carefully arranged. A generic and a specific name and the essential characteristics of each species were given, its native country was indicated, and synonyms were noted for the name of every plant of which Linnaeus had sufficient knowledge. Other authorities who had classified the plant, and other books where it was mentioned, were also listed.

155

Thus the entry for *Nicotiana tabacum* (tobacco) looked like this:

NICOTIANA

Tabacum 1. NICOTIANA foliis lanceolatis. *Hort. cliff.* 56. *Hort. ups.* 45. *Mat. med.* 87; *Roy. lugdb.* 423.
Nicotiana major latifolia. *Bauh. pin.* 169.
Blennochoes. *Reneal. spec.* 37. t. 38.
Habitat in America, *nota Europaeis ab 1560.*

Foliis lanceolatis means "with lanceolate (narrow, lance-shaped) leaves." *Hort. cliff. 56, Hort. ups. 45, Mat. med. 87,* refer to three books of Linnaeus', and the pages where the plant is mentioned. The books are *Hortus Cliffortianus, Hortus Upsaliensis,* and *Materia Medica. Roy lugdb., Bauh. pin.,* and *Reneal. spec.* refer to books by other authors. *Nicotiana major latifolia* and *Blennochoes* are synonyms for the plant. *Habitat in America, nota Europaeis ab 1560* means "native in America, known in Europe since 1560."

But *Species Plantarum* was most important of all for its daring reformation of the scientific names of plants. In this work, Linnaeus definitely cast off forever the old hampering, lengthy names and substituted instead his binomial system — a name of two parts for each plant,

Hyofcyamus vulgaris & niger. *Bauh. pin.* 169.
Habitat in Europæ *ruderatis pinguibus.* ♂

albus. 2. HYOSCYAMUS fóliis petiolatis, floribus feffilibus.
Hort. cliff. 56. *Roy. lugdb.* 422. *Sauv. monfp.* 275.
Hyofcyamus albus major. *Bauh. pin.* 169.
β Hyofcyamus albus minor. *Bauh. pin.* 169.
Hyofcyamus albus vulgaris. *Cluf. hift.* 2. *p.* 118.
Habitat in Europa *auftrali.* ☉

aureus. 3. HYOSCYAMUS foliis petiolatis, floribus peduncu-
latis. *Hort. cliff.* 56. *Roy. lugdb.* 422.
Hyofcyamus creticus luteus major. *Bauh. pin.* 169.
prodr. 92.
β. Hyofcyamus creticus luteus minor. *Bauh. pin.* 169.
Hyofcyamus aureus. *Alp. exot.* 99. *t.* 98.
Habitat in Creta. ☉

pufillus. 4. HYOSCYAMUS foliis lanceolatis fubdentatis, calycibus fpinofis. *Hort. upf.* 44.
Hyofcyamus foliis lanceolatis. *Hort. cliff.* 56. *Roy. lugdb.*
422.
Hyofcyamus pufillus aureus americanus, antirrhini foliis
glabris. *Pluk. alm.* 188. *t.* 37. *f.* 5.
Habitat in Perfia. ☉

phyfalodes. 5. HYOSCYAMUS foliis ovatis integerrimis, calycibus
inflatis fubglobofis. *Hort. upf.* 44. *

Habitat in Sibiria. ♃

NICOTIANA.

Tabacum. 1. NICOTIANA foliis lanceolatis. *Hort. cliff.* 56. *Hort.*
upf. 45. *Mat. med.* 87. *Roy. lugdb.* 423.
Nicotiana major latifolia. *Bauh. pin.* 169.
Blennochoes. *Reneal. fpec.* 37. *t.* 38.
Habitat in America, *nota Europæis ab* 1560. ☉

ruftica. 2. NICOTIANA foliis ovatis. *Hort. cliff.* 56. *Hort. upf.*
45. *Roy. lugdb.* 423.
Nicotiana minor. *Bauh. pin.* 170.
Pachyphylla. *Reneal. fpec.* 40.
Habitat in America, *nunc in Europa.* ☉

paniculata. 3. NICOTIANA foliis cordatis, floribus paniculatis: tu-
bis clavatis.
Nicotiana minor, folio cordiforum tubo floris prælon-
go. *Fewill. peruv.* 1. *p.* 717. *t.* 10.

Ha-

one for its genus and one for its species. The specific name appeared in italics in the left-hand margin. In this case, it is *Tabacum*.

Quite often, as he had advised in *Critica Botanica*, Linnaeus kept the old Latin or Greek name as that of the genus. But he devised a specific name to express something striking about the plant, so that the scientific name would have meaning for the student of botany.

Sometimes the names were descriptive. For instance, he included an oak tree with the botanical name *Quercus alba*. It was so called because *Quercus* is the Latin word for "oak"; *alba* means "white" in Latin, and this oak has light-gray, nearly white, bark. In everyday language, *Quercus alba* is the white oak.

Sometimes the names indicated the men who discovered the plants or who were identified with them in some way. As was mentioned earlier, the genus *Nicotiana* commemorates the French diplomat Nicot. The *Gardenia* was named for Dr. Alexander Garden, an American who sent the plant to Linnaeus.

In some cases the name pointed to the country where the plant was native. *Ulmus americana*, for instance, is the white elm. It received its scientific name because *Ulmus* is the Latin word for "elm," and the tree was found in America — hence, *americana*.

Or sometimes the plant names might be a combination of any of the above things. Linnaeus gave the Persian lilac the name *Syringa persica*. *Persica* indicates

that the plant was from Persia. *Syringa* is a Latinization
of the Greek word *syrinx,* a tubular shepherd's pipe.
The lilac received this name because a plant similar to it
had a tubular stem.

Species Plantarum was a tremendous work — a turning point in the science of botany. It represented years
of meticulous and scholarly labor on Linnaeus' part. It
was a systematic account of what was known scientifi-
cally about the world's plants at that time, and it introduced a practical means of discussing them. With
Linnaeus' binomial system the scientific names of plants
could be more easily remembered than ever before, and
they could also be more easily spoken and written.

Moreover, Linnaeus' short systematic descriptions
identifying each species, and his use of one constant
name for each genus — for instance, *Ulmus* for all elms
— also made recognition and classification of new species
easier. (The generic descriptions are not given in *Species Plantarum.* The book was intended to be used with
the fifth edition of *Genera Plantarum.*)

Ever since Linnaeus' day the binomial system of naming plants has been followed. Of *Species Plantarum* he
himself said: "By such a book everyone could see what
had already been discovered and what was new, when
it occurred, and how it were rightly to be named, which
otherwise was not possible."

He also spoke of his naming of species by what are
now called specific names. He called them trivial names,

and said of them, "He [Linnaeus] put such on all plants. It was the same as to put a clapper in the bell; hereby botany got new life. Now the names would not only be easily remembered, but also be spoken and written with ease which previously was made through definitions. By this means botany got quite a new and natural form."

At about this same time, Linnaeus received an offer from Spain, suggesting that he take the position of Chief of the Spanish Royal College of Medicine, and Director of the Museum and Botanical Garden. It was a well-paid post, and Linnaeus was pleased to be recognized as suitable for it, but he decided to refuse, feeling that he should remain in Sweden.

In 1754, Linnaeus' second son, Johannes, was born. Besides his first-born, Carl, he was already the father of three girls: Elizabeth Christina, born in 1743; Louisa, born in 1750; and Sara Christina, born in 1751. The year 1754 was one of illness for the family, and Linnaeus was plunged into gloom and worry when his wife and the children were all seized with severe fever during the winter. "It is trying to be the father of a family," he wrote a friend.

His work went well, however, and attendance at his public lectures reached a high point. Sometimes as many as two hundred and fifty students crowded the botanical garden as he talked.

During the whole year of 1756 he worked at his tenth edition of *Systema Naturae*. As his knowledge in the field of natural history broadened, this book had grown progressively larger with each new edition. Never content to rest on past work, Linnaeus constantly labored to improve his books. At the Linnean Society in London there are some of his own printed copies of his works, annotated in his crabbed handwriting. The faded brown ink of his notes testifies to his probing, self-critical, always restless mind. Here on the page of a book a printed line is crossed out and a new one is written in; there a new plant name is substituted for an old one; sometimes a written note is pasted into the proper place where a correction should be made; occasionally a whole page is crossed out and rewritten. These are Linnaeus' own working copies of his books; the notes indicate the changes he wished to make in the next edition.

As, in 1756, he worked on *Systema Naturae*, Linnaeus was still trying out new ideas. In this edition he began to apply his binomial system to animals as well as to plants. Again he was a pioneer, laying the foundations for the modern scientific names used by zoologists.

In that same year he was saddened by three deaths. Olaf Celsius, who had helped him so much in his younger years, died. Closer to home was the death of Linnaeus' little son Johannes, two years old, after an illness of only eight days. In July came news that Peter Löfling had died in Venezuela the year before. When Löfling's journal was sent home it was edited by Linnaeus and later published. "Of all my apostles," said Linnaeus, "none has gone so far as he. Therefore I grieve for him heartily."

In November, 1756, a happier time came when Linnaeus' fourth daughter, Sophia, was born. Apparently dead at birth, she was revived, and lived to be her father's favorite. As she grew older he took her with him on his walks around the countryside, and often the little girl accompanied him to his classes, where she stood between his knees as he lectured.

THE BELOVED
TEACHER-BOTANIST

IN 1758, LINNAEUS BOUGHT HAMMARBY, A
small farm near Uppsala. This was to be his
country home for the remainder of his life. It
was a pleasant place, and here the family spent
their summers.

Sara Elizabeth was a good housewife, but she
took no interest in science. Probably Linnaeus
did not encourage her to. He had little liking for
intellectual women and would not even allow his

daughters to go to school. The story is told that, during a time when he was in Stockholm, his wife decided to send Sophia to school. He returned home to find the little girl gone. When he learned her whereabouts he went to the school and asked the teacher to give the girls a half-holiday. He could be a merry companion, and when the little girls were dismissed, he joined them in games. This same procedure went on for several days. Then, by mutual consent, Sophia was taken out of school.

Linnaeus' daughters were by no means entirely ignorant, however. Linnaeus was generous in asking the poverty-stricken students in his classes to share the family's meals. He himself, in his student days, had often gone hungry, and he remembered with gratitude the men who had befriended him. Although Linnaeus always cautioned his young guests not to lend the girls books that would give them too much learning, still his daughters did grow up in a household where they heard ideas discussed and where study and intellectual inquiry were an accepted part of living. They were pleasant companions, although they had no formal teaching.

Though Linnaeus was chary of his daughters becoming scholars, he was just the opposite with his son Carl. Perhaps he made learning too easy for the boy. Instead of going to school where he would have had discipline and competition with boys his own age, young Carl had as his tutors various of Linnaeus' students. Among them was Peter Löfling, who took the position during his university years. Löfling had little money and had been able to support himself at the university only with the greatest difficulty. When Linnaeus offered him board and room in return for teaching young Carl, the chance seemed heaven-sent to Löfling. He gave the boy an excellent grounding in botany.

The daily routine of Linnaeus and his family was much enlivened by the many pets that lived in the house at Uppsala and in the adjoining botanical garden. Linnaeus loved animals, and they had a scientific fascination for him besides. The live animals in the garden were kept partly as aids to him in the teaching of zoology. Many of them had been given him by the king and queen. There were an ape and her young, a monkey, guinea pigs, a number of parrots, two raccoons, an agouti from South America, Muscovy ducks, guinea hens, a cockatoo, peacocks, and a young orangutan. Many of the animals were rare in Europe, and most of Linnaeus' students had never before seen their like. To come to the botanical garden in a country as far north as Sweden, to enter a tropical greenhouse and see a banana plant in flower, to watch an ape and her offspring or a jungle orangutan, and to listen to Linnaeus talk of them all in his witty way — this was almost a miracle to the young students from the provinces and certainly was a far cry from the usual drab academic lecture. It is no wonder that his pupils adored Linnaeus. He opened

Linnaeus smoking his pipe. From a lithograph drawn by J. E. Rehn
in 1747.

their eyes to the great world around them and sent their thoughts winging.

Among the favorite household pets of Linnaeus and his children were Sjup, a raccoon, and Grinn, a monkey. Grinn had belonged to the royal family, but had finally been banished because of his habit of snatching the silver buckles off the courtiers' shoes. One particular parrot was also a great favorite in the household. He sat on his master's shoulder during family meals and was given a bite to eat now and then. When the bird was hungry and no food seemed to be in preparation, he took matters in hand, shouting, "Twelve o'clock, Mr. Carl," as the servants did when they announced the midday meal.

Linnaeus also had a favorite dog, Pompey, who even went to church with his master. At Hammarby, Linnaeus went to the Dannmark parish church. He was accustomed to walk to services, stopping on the way at a certain rock to smoke his pipe. When he continued toward church he left his pipe in a clump of bushes and picked it up on his return. Usually he stayed in church for about an hour, leaving if the sermon went on too long. Even on those occasions when Linnaeus did not go to church, Pompey followed the usual routine, stopping at the rock, sitting quietly alone on the Hammarby bench in church for about an hour, then returning home.

Sara Elizabeth seems to have been hospitable to all the animals except one kind: crickets. Linnaeus loved

Carl Linnaeus in his later years.

their chirping and liked to hide a few in the house to lull him to sleep at night. Sara Elizabeth always managed to find them and put them out. But it did no good. Linnaeus only hastened to secure a fresh supply.

One of his students, Johann Fabricius, has left a description of Linnaeus and his daily life. "For two whole years," Fabricius wrote, "I had the privilege and pleasure of listening to his teaching, his advice, and his friendly conversation. Not a day went by without my seeing him and hearing his lectures, and often talking with him informally for several hours. In summer we three foreigners — Kuhn, an American; and Zoega and I, Danish — went with him into the country.

"In winter we had rooms close to him, and he came to see us almost every day in a short red dressing gown and a green fur cap, with a pipe in his hand. He came for 'half an hour,' but willingly stayed longer — for one or almost two hours. His conversation was lively and pleasant. Either he told us anecdotes of the scholars and scientists he had known, or he answered our questions on scientific matters. He laughed a great deal and his face was smiling and happy, plainly showing his high spirits and his enjoyment of company and friendship.

"Our life was still happier in the country. We lived near Hammarby in a farmer's cottage where we had set up our own household. Linnaeus came to us at about six A.M., as he had building going on at his house. He had breakfast with us and lectured us on the natural orders of plants for as long as we liked, generally until about ten o'clock. Then we walked to the rocks and fields nearby, which under his guidance provided us with many subjects of interest. In the late afternoon we visited him in his garden, and in the evening usually played trisett with his wife. This was her favorite card game.

"On Sundays the whole family came to our place, and sometimes we asked a countryman to come with a fiddle, to which we danced in the barn. Our balls were not particularly brilliant, not many people were present, and the music was poor, but we danced in turn minuets and polkas and enjoyed ourselves. . . . Linnaeus sometimes, though seldom, even danced a polka, in which he outdid all us youngsters. Unless he saw that we were gay, and even noisy, he feared that we were not having a good time. None of us will ever forget those delightful days and hours. I recall with gratitude how much I have to thank him for, both for his instruction and for his gracious behavior."

Fabricius further says of Linnaeus: "He was an excellent companion, pleasant in conversation, full of bits of fancy and entertaining stories; but at the same time suddenly roused to anger, and boisterous; the sudden bursting forth of this fiery passion subsided, however, almost as soon as it started, and he immediately became all plain good nature again. His friendship was sure and unchanging. Science was generally its basis. . . . His way of living was moderate and parsimonious, his dress plain and oftentimes even shabby. . . . His greatest excellence was the systematic order of his thought. Whatever he did or said was faithful to order, truth, and regularity."

Linnaeus took great pains with his foreign pupils; he had been a stranger in a foreign country himself and he had great sympathy for these young men far from home. But he also was tremendously proud that from distant parts of the world — America, Siberia, North Africa — young students should have come to Uppsala, a little town tucked away in Sweden, merely because he was there. He made these young men welcome and became their true friend. And he gave all of himself to teaching them. The fame of Uppsala spread, and the interest in botany grew enormously. These were enchanted years for the university. With Rosén teaching medicine, and Linnaeus, natural history, Uppsala flourished as never before. The usual number of students had been about five hundred, but in 1759, when Linnaeus served a short term as Rector, there were fifteen hundred students, from many countries.

From all over the world, too, plants and seeds continued to come to Linnaeus. In his autobiography he writes: "In no garden has ever been sowed so many kinds of seeds as in that of Uppsala during my time, having got seeds from all the curious in the whole world. . . .

"All botanists did as it were contend to send me one of each kind of new and rare plant in order to hear my opinion and to gratify me with something remarkable."

Letters to his many botanical friends and from them are full of mention of seeds sent, seeds wanted, seeds waylaid on sailing ships by pirates, seeds damaged in transit, plants received in good condition, plants suffering from too long an ocean voyage, offers of an exchange of plants — even slight cases of bribery in which Linnaeus offers to name the plant for the donor if only he may have it.

In our day, when botanical gardens are well established in all large cities, reading these letters is a vivid reminder of how much the botanists of Linnaeus' period accomplished through their dedicated search for knowledge.

Linnaeus also worked constantly at his herbarium. He had all the plants he had collected in his youth; those from Lapland; from Clifford's garden at Hartecamp; from his travels in Holland, England, and France; from Siberia, Kamchatka, and the northern part of America; from Jamaica, a collection he bought in 1758; from Spain; from Egypt and Palestine; from the East Indies — the list could go on almost indefinitely. Linnaeus was not bragging when he said: "The Linnaeus herbarium is without doubt the greatest collection ever seen." For his day it was a truly remarkable array of plants.

Many of the specimens in his herbarium may be seen at London's Linnean Society today. Faded and brown and fragile though they may be, they are still sought out by botanists who wish an original type specimen to compare with a certain plant they may have. The plants are dried and pasted onto sheets of paper. The Latin names are handwritten in ink, now rather faded.

The brownish leaves and blossoms and the faint, spidery writing still speak across the centuries, however. As we look at these plants that grew green in the sunlight of over two centuries ago, a picture comes to mind of a short, vigorous young man striding across a field, his head bent and his sharp brown eyes searching the ground for some small blossoming plant he may not have seen before.

ADVANCING YEARS

EVER SINCE HIS TRUSTED GARDENER,
Dietrich Nietzel, had died in 1756, Linnaeus had
worried about the botanical garden. No Swedish
gardener could be found who had Nietzel's experience with rare tropical plants, and the salary
was not sufficient to attract a good man from another country. After several incompetent garden-
ers had attempted to fill the position and after
several irreplaceable plants had been lost by their

bungling, Linnaeus decided that steps must be taken to remedy the situation and relieve his own mind. Already overworked, he was often sick with anxiety over the well-being of his beloved garden.

In the autumn of 1758 he suggested to the chancellor of the university that the post of Demonstrator be created. Many foreign botanical gardens had a man who filled such a position. The Demonstrator would keep in touch with foreign botanists, secure new seeds, teach the students, supervise the care of the garden, and take charge of the university's natural history museum. Up to this time, Linnaeus had undertaken all these tasks himself.

The scheme was finally approved. Early in 1759, Linnaeus further suggested that his son Carl, now nineteen years old, should be appointed to the post of Demonstrator. As yet, no money had been set aside for a salary, so Linnaeus suggested that in the meantime the young man should give his services free. Linnaeus was anxious to train someone in the work as soon as possible, as the Demonstrator must learn the growing habits of thousands of foreign plants. Thoughts of the terrible loss to the garden if he should die and there should be no one with an understanding of the individual plants and their needs haunted Linnaeus.

Although there was some private grumbling around the university that this arrangement was "all in the family," actually it was a sensible plan. Young Carl had

Portrait of Carl Linnaeus by Orata.

been brought up in the garden and knew its contents thoroughly. He had a good grounding in botany already, and Linnaeus now intended to work with him and make a genuine botanist of him. In the meantime the elder Linnaeus could breathe more easily, now that another person was learning to share his responsibilities.

Besides his worries about the garden, Linnaeus was anxious about money. Although Sara Elizabeth had a good income from her family, the purchase of Hammarby and other property in 1758 had left him with financial problems.

Some years before, he had submitted to the government a scheme for producing cultured pearls. At the time of his journey to Lapland he had watched the pearl fishing at Purkijaur, and the thought had come to him that perhaps artificial means might be used to make the river mussels produce pearls. Since then, he had experimented with mussels in the river at Uppsala and had hit upon a way of making pearls. He had shown some of his products to a jeweler, who had pronounced them of particularly good quality. They were produced by attaching a tiny ball of limestone to a thin silver wire and inserting it through a small hole bored in the mussel's shell. The wire was secured to the shell, and the mussel was returned to the river. After about six years a large pearl had been formed as the mussel covered the irritating bit of limestone with layers of nacreous material.

When Linnaeus had first submitted his plan to the

government, there had been no interest. But in 1761 he was asked to restate his scheme. He appeared before a government committee in Stockholm and showed his pearls, explaining the method of production. More than one year went by before a decision was reached about his idea, but finally, in 1762, Linnaeus was awarded over two thousand dollars — a large sum of money in those days. In addition, he was granted the right at some future date to give up his professorship to his son or to any other person whom he thought qualified to hold it. The method of making pearls was to be kept secret unless the king and Parliament should decide otherwise. Soon after, Parliament sold the secret to a merchant for the same sum it had paid Linnaeus. The end result was satisfactory to one and all. Linnaeus had gained a sizable sum of money and security for his son, and the government had been repaid the money it had spent.

In 1762, also, Linnaeus received confirmation that he had been knighted by the king. As a nobleman, he took the name of von Linné — a name by which he is often known in Sweden today.

As a nobleman, too, Linnaeus was required to have a coat of arms. On it he wished to have pictured his favorite little plant, *Linnaea borealis,* and also to have a three-colored background representing the three fields of nature, with a halved egg thereon, because "nature is continued in an egg." But heraldry is a complicated and rather rigid business and follows set rules. The king at

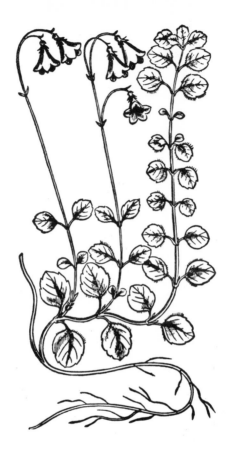

Probably the first Swedish illustration of the
twinflower, *Linnaea borealis,* from a woodcut
published by Olof Rudbeck, about 1720.

arms, who made final decisions on such matters as coats of arms, found all sorts of things wrong with Linnaeus' plan. An argument followed, during which Linnaeus made bitter remarks about "scrambled eggs." Finally another plan was arrived at, awarding Linnaeus a coat of arms that showed three crowns, with an animal on one, a plant on another, and a stone on a third.

In that same year, 1762, the French Scientific Academy made him one of its eight foreign Fellows. He had been the Swedish correspondent of the Academy for many years, but the appointment as Fellow was a high honor, which he cherished.

Linnaeus had long been weary from overwork and poor health, and in 1763 the university granted him leave from service, although he promised to continue with his teaching as long as he was physically able. In his place as Professor of Botany he appointed his son Carl, planning to supervise the younger man and fit him completely for the post.

Carl had taken no examinations. Consequently there was great dissatisfaction among the students over his appointment, as well as severe criticism of Linnaeus. But the government had given the elder man the right to choose his successor and he sincerely believed young Carl competent for the post. At one time he had halfway offered the position to Daniel Solander, one of his students. Solander preferred to live in England, however, and had been promised a fine position at the British

Museum. In addition, he had been appointed naturalist for Joseph Banks's ship, *Endeavour,* on her voyage around the world. So young Carl Linnaeus became Professor of Botany at Uppsala.

It was not a satisfactory arrangement for him. His father was to keep the salary and all the privileges of the professorship during his lifetime, and the elder Linnaeus also continued with his lecturing except during times when he definitely was ill.

One of these times came in 1764 when he had a severe attack of fever and pleurisy. Rosén attended him constantly, and Linnaeus gave the physician full credit for his recovery. Thereafter, the two former rivals who had been so slow to accept each other became firm friends and enjoyed mutual understanding and pleasant companionship for the remainder of their lives.

In that same year, Linnaeus and his wife celebrated their twenty-fifth wedding anniversary. Three days later, their eldest daughter, Elizabeth Christina, was married to Fredrik Bergenkrantz, a lieutenant in the Upland regiment. He was a grandson of Linnaeus' old friend Olof Rudbeck, and the botanist was pleased by the match.

But sad news soon cast him into a period of gloom. In September, 1764, he received word of the death of another of his apostles. On Linnaeus' special advice, Peter Forskål, a Finnish student, had gone out with an expedition of Danish scientists to Egypt and Arabia. He had been on his way home when he died of the plague.

In October came a letter to Linnaeus, almost as if from the dead. He had asked Forskål to find him a specimen of the small evergreen Mecca tree, then unknown to European botanists. In the letter were a stalk and flower of the tree, with a description of it, dispatched before Forskål's death. Linnaeus was deeply touched by this reminder of his pupil's faithfulness, and named a plant after him: *Forskohlea*. Some people complained that it was undistinguished-looking and did little credit to Forskål. But Linnaeus had intended an honor to his pupil, as *Forskohlea* was unusual and interesting botanically.

In 1765, a pleasant gift came to Linnaeus from one of his former students, J. P. Falck, who was then Professor of Medicine and Director of the Botanical Garden at the College of Medicine in St. Petersburg, Russia. Falck sent his former teacher a fine collection of plants for his herbarium and seeds for his garden.

During the summer of 1766, Linnaeus went for the last time to arrange the queen's collection of natural history specimens. Then his life settled down to a quiet routine of teaching and writing, with an occasional visit to Stockholm.

Linnaeus' writing at this time was partly new work and partly the always important revisions of his earlier books. Among others, he worked on the twelfth, and last, edition of *Systema Naturae*, which had first been printed as a modest-appearing little book in Holland in 1735, when Linnaeus was just starting his career. Both Linnaeus and the book had grown ever since. The last *Systema Naturae* was published in 1767 as a huge work in several volumes.

In 1766 there had been another serious fire in Uppsala, and Linnaeus had feared for his collections of books and natural history objects. Two years later, he had a small museum built on a little hill near his house at Hammarby. He used this as a working place and sitting room in summer, and spoke of it as his "pleasure house." Here he received visitors, some of them famous people who had come from afar to see him. One of these visitors was Lord Baltimore, from America. He is said to have arrived in an English traveling coach so enormous that it was necessary to take down the gateposts on the road to Hammarby in order to allow it to pass.

In 1771, King Adolphus Frederick of Sweden died, and Linnaeus lost a good friend and patron. The queen's power was much lessened with her husband's death. Their son Gustavus III succeeded to the throne. He had spent a good deal of time in Paris and was interested in making the court a center of art and fashion. He had little of his parents' strong interest in science and education. In the years to come, Uppsala suffered on this account.

Linnaeus was now in his sixties, and ailing. His fame and genius and his own lively wit still drew crowds to

An old engraving of Carl Linnaeus standing in his museum. This picture emphasizes his short, stocky build.

the university, but his age was beginning to tell. In 1772 he noted that he was often dizzy and frequently stumbled, especially with his right foot. As a medical man, he read the symptoms: a slight stroke. He took his fate philosophically, noting that he had labored hard all his life both with his body and with his mind, and that he was thoroughly worn out. "The stroke has left me feeble and timid," he wrote a friend.

He did sincerely try to work less hard, but found it maddening to be idle. Though he permitted his son to lecture in his stead, after one term of leisure Linnaeus found himself forgetful and slow in thought. He was like an old cart horse who grew stiff in the legs from standing, he remarked. So back to work he went. Presently he was serving as Rector of the university and was writing to a friend that he was preparing a variety of works: orations, disputations, private lectures, a new book, and "six hundred other things."

At the end of 1772, when his term as Rector was over, he made the customary oration. It was entitled, *"Deliciae Naturae"* ("Delights of Nature"). It so pleased his listeners that the next day the students sent a committee to thank their dear professor. He was flattered and proud, remarking that it was "a thing which never happened to anyone else." In fact, his whole six-month period as Rector had been a pleasure; out of respect for the aging man the students had been quiet and orderly and had kept from their usual high jinks and skylarking.

The beginning of the new year, 1773, brought ill health again — this time an attack of sciatica. Linnaeus did bestir himself to go to Stockholm, where the Swedish Royal Bible Commission was working to make a more accurate translation of the Bible. He had an encyclopedic knowledge of the plants mentioned in the scriptures and of their uses. His help was invaluable to the commission, but the trip was almost too much for him to endure. It tired him more than the whole of his long-ago journey to Lapland, he declared.

His stay-at-home days were brightened by letters from his pupils in countries all over the world. He had taught them to report carefully on what they found, and they wrote him not only about plants but also about the people and places they visited and the customs they observed. These letters were more than detailed reports, however. They were warm, affectionate outpourings from the students to the friend and teacher whom they loved and respected. To Linnaeus, sick and worn, they brought a world of youthful excitement and discovery and goodwill. He wrote long, friendly letters in reply to these young men who were following in his footsteps.

There were triumphs, too, to cheer his heart. In the large botanical gardens of Europe, labels were being placed, giving the plants' generic and specific names according to Linnaeus' system. A little earlier, the King of France had ordered the garden at the Trianon labeled in this way. And even at the Paris Botanic Garden,

Buffon, the current superintendent, who was a stern critic of the Linnaean system, was obliged to do the same.

Then suddenly, one bright day in May, Linnaeus had a dangerous stroke as he was lecturing in the garden to a group of his private pupils. He knew he never would be completely well again. He recovered somewhat, but moved about with slowness and difficulty.

Christmas in 1775 was a happy time. King Gustavus III, although not a natural scientist himself, remembered Sweden's great botanist by sending him sixteen large chests full of South American plants, flowers, and fruits bottled in spirits. Nothing could have given Linnaeus more satisfaction. He lost no time in looking through his treasures, and found many new genera and species.

A few months later, Governor Tulbagh sent him an enormous collection of dried plants, bulbs, and seeds from the Cape of Good Hope. Many of them had been previously unknown to botanists. To honor the governor for his generous present, Linnaeus gave the generic name *Tulbaghia* to one of the bulb plants. At about the same time, one of his apostles sent him a plant collection from China. Events like these rallied Linnaeus' spirits and made him, for a while at least, as gay and lively as he had been in former years.

But his health was failing rapidly now, although he continued with a few lectures in 1776. His sharp mind

Carl Linnaeus, a few years before his death. Portrait painted by
Roslin in 1775.

was blurring, however, his memory was failing, and his speech was no longer distinct. He mentioned himself in his diary, saying that he limped and could hardly walk, that he spoke unintelligibly, and was scarcely able to write. He further described himself at this time as being a little below common size, with a frame that was strong and solid, but rather stooped when walking — from his habit of looking for plants. His eyes were brown and piercing, his sight sharp, and his ear acute at catching every sound. He mentioned his memory, saying that it had been strong in his youth, but had become dulled after the age of sixty.

Linnaeus had asked to be allowed to retire, but because of the prestige he lent the university the king was reluctant to let him go. In May, 1776, the botanist again begged that his son take over the teaching. He promised still to oversee the botanical garden and do a few other small duties. This time the king granted his wish.

From that time on, Linnaeus' health declined rapidly and his brain was often befogged. He spent the summer of 1777 at Hammarby. Every day in good weather he was carried out into the garden. He had cultivated a grove near the house, and liked to sit in a clearing in the midst of it. His daughter's children called it "Grandfather's bower." When the wind stirred the branches, the glass bells that had been hung among the trees played a soft and subtle melody, sweet to his ears.

On overcast days he lay in his museum among his

natural history treasures. Being among the things of nature that he knew so well and to which he had devoted his life seemed always to make him brighter and happier.

In the autumn he was even able to walk a bit and could be taken for drives around the countryside. But this was only a temporary rally, and with the coming of cold weather his mind and body slowed still more.

On the morning of January 10, 1778, he finally died — almost seventy-one years of age. With him at the time of his death were one of his pupils and the fiancé of his youngest daughter, Sophia.

In a sealed envelope he had left instructions for his burial: "Let the great bell of the cathedral be tolled, but not in the other churches or country churches, or the hospital, save in Dannmark's church." This was his parish church at Hammarby.

"Let a thanksgiving to God who granted me so many years and blessings be held both in the cathedral and Dannmark's church. Let my countrymen [the men of Småland] bear me to the grave, and give to each of them a little medal of one of those cast with my portrait."

Two years before, he had ordered a great elm to be cut on the Hammarby estate, to provide wood for his coffin. In this he was borne to the cathedral at six o'clock in the evening on January 22. One of the mourners has left an account of the final services:

"It was dark and still. The gloom was pierced only in

those parts of the town where the slow-moving procession of mourners passed, bearing torches and lanterns. The silence was broken only by the low murmurs of the crowds and the sad tolling of the great majestic bell. . . . A huge company, including the entire university, was in the procession. Many doctors of medicine, all former pupils of Linnaeus, bore the great man to his grave."

The church was lit only by candles, with which all the candelabra were filled. "I never saw so many people in the building as on this occasion," wrote one observer.

In the cathedral, as the organ rang out, Linnaeus was laid to rest. His grave is under the organ loft on the north side of the building. It is marked by a monument erected by his friends and students. On it is an inscription in Latin. Translated, it reads: *Carl von Linné. The Prince of Botany. From his friends and disciples.*

LINNAEUS TODAY

IN WRITING OF HIMSELF, LINNAEUS HAS SAID
that he "read on the earth, stones, vegetables,
and animals as in a book." An acute observer,
he made natural history his province and so interested himself in many things. He was perhaps
the first botanist to call attention to the so-called
"sleep" of plants — the changes that occur in
some species during darkness.

192

He paid more attention than previous botanists had to the natural habitats of plants, noting the places where they were native and grew wild, and even the kind of soil they required, where this was possible.

In his book *Pan and Pandora* he attempted to list what plant each noncarnivorous animal and insect ate. "It is the ground to the pastoral life," he said.

He even seems to have had some glimmerings of what we now call ecology — the subtle relationships that exist among living organisms and between them and their environment. As he put it, he showed "the combination that exists between the created things, as to their production, conservation, and destruction."

Before his time, little had been known about the plants and animals of Sweden. It was he, through his reports of his travels in his native land and through his books *Flora Suecica* and *Fauna Suecica*, who first opened the eyes of the Swedish people to their own natural history.

He did much to systematize the study of zoology and make it a science. "Before Linnaeus' time," he wrote, "zoology was an Augean stable filled up with tables and nonsense, far from being a science or a systematical work."

But it is in the science of botany that Linnaeus will remain forever immortal.

It has been argued by some botanical historians that he made no important botanical discoveries of his own, but merely adopted the work of other men and fashioned it into a system.

His predecessors had made important findings, but their work was scattered and incomplete. Linnaeus was eminently fitted to do exactly what was needed in his time. He drew together the many strands of the botany up to his day, scrutinizing, analyzing, criticizing them, discarding the foolishness and adding his own sharp observations, and making of them an intelligible whole. He cut the prolix descriptions of plants to their important essentials, and in *Systema Naturae* devised a workable grouping of plants. True, it was an artificial grouping and did not arrange plants according to their natural relationships, but he himself realized this.

"I am ready to agree with you that the stamens and pistils lead to no natural system," he wrote his friend Dr. Albert Haller in 1737, "having adopted a method founded thereon as a substitute, to excite curious observers to examine these parts of fructification, hitherto reckoned as trifling and unimportant; for an alphabetical arrangement was always intolerable to me. Besides, an attention to the organs in question may have its use, though not altogether for the purpose of natural classes.

". . . If my harmless sexual system be the only cause of offense, I cannot but protest against so much injustice. I have never spoken of that as a natural method: on the contrary, in my *Systema* I have said. 'No natural botanical system has yet been constructed, though one or two may be more so than others; nor do I contend that this system is by any means natural. Probably I may, on a future occasion, propose some fragments of such a one. . . . Meanwhile, till that is discovered, artificial systems are indispensable.' "

All his life, Linnaeus strove to perfect a better system of classification, but it must be remembered that plant relationships were not so clearly understood in his time as they are today. *On the Origin of Species,* Charles Darwin's classic statement of his thoughts on natural selection and evolution, was still about one hundred years in the future. When Linnaeus first started his work, he conceived of species as having been so created by God in the beginning of time. As the years went by and he observed varieties and mutations his doubts of this idea grew, but he never was able fully to resolve his difficulties on this score.

Today Linnaeus' sexual classification no longer stands as valid. Modern botanists, with their knowledge of evolution, have tried to make natural classifications of plants, grouping together those that are apparently most closely related to each other and have some plant ancestry in common. This is a difficult task, never completely satisfactory, and the work of natural classification still goes forward. But even though Linnaeus' system of classification is no longer used, it was the all-important beginning step. Without it the science of botany might have developed more slowly.

As to his other work, many of the basic rules for classification that he set forth in *Critica Botanica,* and the binomial method of *Species Plantarum,* are still used today. In 1905, botanists at an international conference agreed that Linnaeus' first edition of *Species Plantarum,* published in 1753, was to be taken as the starting point for modern botanical nomenclature. Botanical names used before 1753 have no standing among modern botanists unless they were adopted by Linnaeus or by later authoritative writers. Many of the Linnaean names are still in use, and *Species Plantarum* remains a classic in its field.

Even today, hundreds of new species of plants are discovered every year. They are usually the particular concern of systematic botanists, who make the classification and naming of plants their work.

First, the newly found plant must be identified. The botanist starts a search, comparing the suspected new species with similar forms, which he finds in an herbarium or in published descriptions. Eventually the plant may be found to have certain definite characteristics so different from any other of its genus that it is classified as a new species. Then it must be described and given a name. The name and description are published in a recognized botanical journal and the specimen is mounted and properly labeled and placed in one of the known herbaria of the world. There it is known as the "type specimen" of the species and may be referred to by other botanists.

The plant is given a name in two parts, generic and specific — a binomial, as Linnaeus recommended. Both words employ the botanical Latin that Linnaeus first devised.

So, even today, Carl Linnaeus stands tall. Although some of his work was careless and much has been discarded, he remains secure in his place among the world's great botanists. He created order out of the chaos of eighteenth-century botany and laid a firm foundation on which later, more informed, scientists still build. His contribution is a lasting one.

SOME IMPORTANT EVENTS IN THE LIFE OF LINNAEUS

1707 — Carl Linnaeus born at Rashult, Sweden, on May 23.

1714 — Placed under the tutorship of Johan Telander.

1716 — Sent with his tutor to Växjö for schooling.

1727 — Enrolled at Lund University on August 19.

1728 — Enrolled at Uppsala University in August.

1729 — Meets Peter Artedi, a fellow student, in March.

1729 — Befriended by Olaf Celsius, and goes to live at his house.

1730 — Presents New Year's greeting to Celsius — treatise on sex in plants.

1730 — Gives his first public botanical lecture in Uppsala botanical garden on May 4.

1730 — Moves to Olof Rudbeck's house to become tutor to his sons.

1731 — Writes Scientific Society at Uppsala, suggesting tour of Lapland; leaves Uppsala for Stenbrohult in December.

1732 — Receives Scientific Society's approval of Lapland trip on April 15.

1732 — Starts Lapland trip on May 12.

1732 — Arrives back at Uppsala from Lapland on October 10.

1733 — Gives private lectures on assaying ores, at Uppsala.

1733 — Spends Christmas holidays in Dalarna with Claes Sohlberg.

1734 — Dalarna expedition, led by Linnaeus, starts on July 3; ends forty-five days later. Linnaeus stays on at Reuterholm's home in Falun.

1734 — Accepts Sohlberg's offer to accompany son abroad; takes theological examination at Uppsala.

1734 — Meets Sara Elizabeth Moraea during Christmas holidays at Falun.

1735 — Becomes informally engaged to Sara Elizabeth Moraea on February 18.

1735 — Sets out for Elsinore, Denmark, with Sohlberg, on first leg of their journey to Holland.

1735 — Arrives with Sohlberg at Amsterdam on June 2; they proceed to Harderwijk several days later.

1735 — *Systema Naturae* published in Leiden.

1735 — Takes employment as doctor-botanist with George Clifford, at Hartecamp, near Haarlem.

1736 — Unexpectedly meets Artedi in Leiden; Artedi drowned in autumn.

1736 — Visits botanists in England, then returns to Hartecamp.

1736 — *Fundamenta Botanica* published.

1736 — *Bibliotheca Botanica* published.

1737 — *Genera Plantarum* published.

1737 — Goes to help von Royen at Leiden Botanical Garden.

1737 — *Flora Lapponica* published.

1737 — *Critica Botanica* published.

1738 — *Classes Plantarum* published.

1738 — *Ichthyologia*, by Peter Artedi, published.

1738 — Leaves Holland for France.

1738 — Returns to Sweden and starts career as physician in Stockholm.

1739 — Appointed lecturer at Royal College in Stockholm.

1739 — Takes position as Physician to the Navy in Stockholm.

1739 — Becomes president of Scientific Society in Stockholm.

1739 — Marries Sara Elizabeth Moraea.

1740 — First child, Carl, born.

1741 — Makes expedition through Öland and Gotland.

1741 — Moves to Uppsala as professor of medicine and anatomy.

Some Important Events in the Life of Linnaeus

1742 — Exchange arranged whereby Linnaeus becomes professor of medicine and botany at Uppsala.

1743 — Daughter, Elizabeth Christina, born.

1745 — *Öland and Gotland Journey* published.

1745 — *Flora Suecica* published.

1746 — *Fauna Suecica* published.

1746 — Makes Västergotland trip.

1746 — Reaches agreement with East India Company whereby students may be sent on expeditions to foreign lands.

1747 — Peter Kalm, a student, leaves for North America.

1748 — *Flora Zeylanica* published.

1749 — Makes tour of province of Skåne.

1750 — Peter Löfling, a student, goes to Spain.

1750 — Daughter, Louisa, born.

1751 — Peter Kalm returns from North America with a fine collection.

1751 — *Philosophia Botanica* published.

1751 — Daughter, Sara Christina, born.

1753 — *Species Plantarum* published.

1754 — Son, Johannes, born.

1755 — Peter Löfling dies in Venezuela.

1756 — Olaf Celsius dies.

1756 — Son, Johannes, dies.

1756 — Daughter, Sophia, born.

1758 — Buys Hammarby, a country home near Uppsala.

1759 — Young Carl Linnaeus appointed assistant to his father, as Demonstrator.

1762 — Knighted; takes name von Linné.

1762 — Made foreign Fellow of the French Scientific Academy.

1763 — Young Carl Linnaeus appointed professor of botany, to succeed his father eventually.

1767 — Twelfth edition of *Systema Naturae* published.

1773 — Goes to Stockholm to work on translation with Swedish Royal Bible Commission.

1776 — Retires as lecturer at Uppsala; his son takes post.

1778 — Dies on January 10; almost seventy-one years old.

INDEX

Index

Index

205

Index

206

Index

207

Index

Index